An Introduction to
ATM Technology

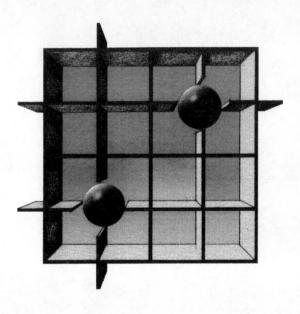

An Introduction to
ATM Technology

Marc Boisseau
Michel Demange
Jean-Marie Munier

IBM France

INTERNATIONAL THOMSON COMPUTER PRESS
I (T) P An International Thomson Publishing Company

London • Bonn • Boston • Johannesburg • Madrid • Melbourne • Mexico City • New York • Paris
Singapore • Tokyo • Toronto • Albany, NY • Belmont, CA • Cincinnati, OH • Detroit, MI

An Introduction to ATM Technology

Copyright ©1995 International Thomson Publishing
Copyright ©1994 Éditions Eyrolles, Paris

I(T)P   A division of International Thomson Publishing Inc.
         The ITP logo is a trademark under licence

British Library Cataloguing-in-Publication Data
A catalogue record for this book is available from the British Library

Library of Congress Cataloging-in-Publication Data
A catalog record for this book is available from the Library of Congress

Commissioning Editor: Liz Israel Oppedijk

The Publisher gratefully acknowledges the help of Dr Christopher S. Cooper of Rutherford Appleton Laboratory in the preparation of this edition.

Printed in the UK by Clays Ltd, St Ives plc
First printed 1995
Reprinted 1995

ISBN 1-850-32140-X

International Thomson Computer Press   International Thomson Computer Press
Berkshire House   20 Park Plaza
High Holborn   14th Floor
London WCIV 7AA   Boston MA 02116
UK   USA

http://www.thomson.com/itcp.html

Imprints of International Thomson Publishing

Contents

Contents   v

Foreword   ix

Preface   xi

1   Switching techniques   1
     1.1 A historical perspective   1
            1.1.1 The ATD technique   3
            1.1.2 The FPS technique   3
            1.1.3 Fast packet switching   4
            1.1.4 The role of the CCITT   5
            1.1.5 The ATM compromise   6
     1.2 The development of telecommunications   8
            1.2.1 Technological features   9
            1.2.2 Planned applications   10

1.2.3 Existing services   11
1.2.4 Constraints   12
   Real time   13
   Bit rate   13
   Quality of service   13

2   Cell relay   **15**
2.1 Principles   15
2.2 ATM layer functions   17
   2.2.1 Principle of cell routing   18
   2.2.2 Protection against congestion   20
      Admission control   21
      Spacing and rate policing   21
      Congestion notification   23
      Discarding   24
   2.2.3 Multiplexing information flows   24
2.3 Functions of the physical layer   24
   2.3.1 Rate adaptation   25
   2.3.2 Header protection by the HEC   25
   2.3.3 Cell delineation   27
      Adaptation by continuous flow of cells   27
      Other bit rate adaptation techniques   28
   2.3.4 Adaptation to the transmission systems   29
      Adaptation to synchronous transmission   29
      Adaptation to plesiochronous transmission
      (Recommendation G.804)   30
      Adaptation to an unframed transmission system   31
   2.3.5 Scrambling cells   31
2.4 Functions of the AAL adaptation layer   32
   2.4.1 Overview   32
   2.4.2 AAL type 1 adaptation function   34
   2.4.3 AAL type 2 adaptation function   38
   2.4.4 AAL type 3/4 adaptation function   38
   2.4.5 AAL type 5 adaptation function   42
2.5 Maintenance flows   44
   2.5.1 Physical layer maintenance flows   44
   2.5.2 ATM layer maintenance flows   46

2.6 Cell relay performance   46

    2.6.1 Loss of cells   46

    2.6.2 Transfer delay   47

       Information coding and decoding   48

       Segmentation and reassembly   48

       Transfer across the network   48

       Global delay target   48

3   ATM switching units   **51**

3.1 Introduction   51

    3.1.1 Circuit switching   51

    3.1.2 Packet switching   52

3.2 ATM switching unit functions   53

    3.2.1 Routing cells   54

    3.2.2 Temporary storage of cells   56

       Input queuing   56

       Output queuing   57

3.3 Types of switching fabric   59

    3.3.1 Shared resource switching units   59

    3.3.2 Space division switching units   60

4   Broadband ISDN   **61**

4.1 Overview   61

4.2 The architecture of broadband ISDN   62

    4.2.1 The configuration reference model   63

    4.2.2 The protocols reference model   65

    4.2.3 Reference points   65

       The interface at reference point T_B 66

       Distribution structure   66

4.3 Signalling systems   68

    4.3.1 Signalling at the user–network interface   68

    4.3.2 Signalling at the network-to-network interface   69

    4.3.3 Metasignalling at the user–network interface   70

4.4 Services offered by broadband ISDN   71

4.5 ATM pilot projects   71

    4.5.1 BT   72

    4.5.2 Deutsche Bundespost Telekom   73

    4.5.3 France Telecom   74

4.5.4 Other broadband trials in Europe   75
4.5.5 ATM in the United States   76

5   ATM and local area networks   **79**
5.1 The development of local area networks   79
5.2 Wiring a site   81
5.3 LAN emulation   82
5.4 Intelligent hubs   83

Appendix   **87**
ATM standardization   87
CCITT   87
ANSI   88
IEEE   89
ATM Forum   89
ETSI   90

Bibliography   **91**

Thematic index   **93**

Index of abbreviations   **97**

Foreword

The 1990s are the decade in which telecommunications will take their revenge on computing. In today's world, telecommunications have become as indispensable as computing, yet their technical progress has been slower: whereas the power of computers has doubled every two years, it has taken the public service network more than 20 years to advance from several kilobits a second to a hundred kilobits a second. However, in the next few years, running up to the millennium, the situation will be reversed: while progress in computing has been slowed by the recession, advances in telecommunications have undergone an extraordinary acceleration, whose effect will be to increase network performance by a factor of several hundred, if not thousand, in just a few years. This spectacular progress is based on advances in key technologies in two areas: physical tele-communication devices – fibre optics, Hertzian or infra-red channels, ultra-high frequency components, either hybrid or opto-electronic – and logical structures – the architectures and protocols required for managing these speeds and integrating information flows with very different characteristics, such as voice, data and video.

Marc Boisseau, Michel Demange and Jean-Marie Munier's book invites us to explore this second area by describing the results of ten years of international research aimed at defining a single solution to the problems of transmitting, switching and multiplexing heterogeneous flows on broadband networks in an economically viable and internationally acceptable way. It is worth underlining the fact that Europe has played a dominant role in the development of ATM (Asynchronous Transfer Mode), starting with the original research at CNET on asynchronous time multiplexing and continuing with the projects in the European Community's RACE programme right up to the present-day experiments on the national and international ATM networks in Germany, Spain, France, Italy, Great Britain and Sweden.

This book explains the various parts of ATM – architecture, flow control, error handling, performance measurement – and describes how the ATM techniques are applied when creating broadband integrated networks, local area networks and exchanges. It is aimed at both the reader who wants a rapid understanding of the basic principles and someone who wants to know the details of the cell formats or the synchronization algorithm. The authors' training, in one of the great telecommunications research laboratories, uniquely equips them for explaining the reasons behind the technical decisions taken by ATM's designers, sometimes not without a certain sense of humour, such as when they reveal that the ATM cell's payload is 48 bytes because 48 is the arithmetic average between 64, proposed by the Americans, and 32, supported by the Europeans... And they do not hesitate to point out the problems that are yet to be solved and the options between which choices will have to be made.

For the first time in many years, a standard in which Europe has played a major part is beginning to impose itself on the worldwide information technology and telecommunications industries. The important thing now is that European industries and economies should be the first to benefit from the intellectual investment made by our researchers, and, in order for this to happen, that ATM should spread rapidly throughout Europe: in higher education, and amongst manufacturers, operators and users. No doubt this comprehensive, clear and precise book will play its part.

Jean-Jacques DUBY
Scientific Director
Union des Assurances de Paris

Preface

ATM (*Asynchronous Transfer Mode*) is a switching, multiplexing and transmission technique which is a variation on packet switching in so far as it uses short, fixed-length packets called **cells**. The handling of the cells in the switching units is limited to analysing their headers so that they can be routed to the appropriate queues. The flow control and error handling functions are not carried out in the ATM network, but are left to the user applications or the access devices.

Because of these characteristics, ATM can respond reasonably to the constraints imposed by traffic as different as voice, moving images or data. This universal transfer mode makes it possible to integrate all types of services on a single network access. Although it was first designed as the technical solution for broadband public networks, ATM is also becoming the technology for future private networks and local area networks.

This book is divided into five chapters and an appendix:

* Chapter 1, **Switching techniques** (page 1), explains the reasons behind the choice of ATM and the resulting possibilities. It is not essential to read this chapter to understand the rest of the book.

- Chapter 2, **Cell relay** (page 15), describes the functions of the ATM layer (routing, multiplexing cells), the underlying physical layers and the layers for adapting cells to various types of application (**AAL**, *ATM Adaptation Layers*).

- Chapter 3, **ATM switching units** (page 51), recalls the principles of conventional switching modes and describes the functions of an ATM **switching unit**. It describes the various techniques for storing cells as well as the types of switching devices.

- Chapter 4, **Broadband ISDN** (page 61), describes the target application for ATM technology in wide area public networks. It also looks at the pilot projects.

- Chapter 5, **ATM and local area networks** (page 79), shows how ATM technology can also be integrated seamlessly into conventional local area networks.

- The Appendix, **ATM standardization** (page 87), describes the work undertaken by the main standardization bodies.

Specific projects, in terms of architectures, systems or products, are beyond the scope of this book.

Switching techniques

1.1 A historical perspective

The technological need for high speed networks is a result of the considerable progress made in computing in the past ten years. This progress has been exemplified by two major changes:

- the change from text based to image based displays;

- the distribution of processing power and data storage.

For telecommunications networks, these two changes imply high bit rates (an image contains at least ten times more basic data items than a text) and extremely short routing delays, if there is to be no impediment to the distribution of computing power and data storage.

One simple way of estimating the needs, in terms of communication capacity, resulting from these changes, is to correlate two empirical laws:

- Joy's law, which states that computing power, expressed in millions of instructions per second (MIPS), doubles every two years, and

- Ruge's law, which estimates that the communication capacity necessary for each MIPS is from 0.3 to 1 Mbits/s.

If we reckon that in 1990 each computer had an average computing power of 100 MIPS, communications needs will increase geometrically in the next few years and reach a value of between 300 Mbits/s and 1 Gbits/s before 2000. Even if average needs are probably ten times less than this, they still largely exceed the capacities of present-day networks, both local and wide area.

High bit rate and short delay are two important characteristics to which we must add a third: the uniformity of the supporting technology, for obvious reasons of both economies of scale and integration. These three criteria formed the objectives of studies carried out in the 1980s.

All the studies assumed that flow control and error handling functions would be dealt with outside the network. This hypothesis was based on the high quality of digital transmission trunks and the inadequacy, at high speed, of protocols that operate hop by hop.

Furthermore, a consensus rapidly emerged around the idea that it should be possible to use a single switching method whatever the type of flow involved.

Frame relay was the first protocol that implemented these principles. It was also at this time that the idea of bridges that forwarded **MAC** (*Medium Access Control*) packets was proposed for interconnecting local area networks.

Amongst these studies, we should mention several important examples: Datakit, AT&T's Voice/Data fast packet switching, IBM's PARIS project, and CNET's Prélude. All these projects used packet switching as their basic concept.

Before we describe the techniques that led to the definition of the ATM transfer mode, it would be useful if we specified the characteristics of the two conventional switching modes:

- **Circuit switching** has the advantage of total data transparency; furthermore, it completely satisfies the real-time requirements of voice and video flows. Therefore, adapting it to high speeds seemed a possibility. However, the disadvantage of this technique is that it only provides circuits with predetermined bit rates (for example, 64 kbits/s channels in the integrated services digital network). Therefore, it would be necessary to plan for a set of fixed bit rates corresponding to the various projected services. Such planning is difficult, even undesirable, because a given service does not necessarily correspond to a specific bit rate, even if it is only because of the improvement, over time, of data compression algorithms. This avenue of research was abandoned because of its lack of flexibility.

- **Packet switching**, based on the notion of the virtual circuit, could provide that adaptability, and make it possible to use communication links efficiently. Frame relay had already shown that communication protocols could be simplified, but whether this principle could be used for flows other than data still needed to be proved. In particular, it still needed to be demonstrated that such a technique could emulate the characteristics of a circuit.

Two avenues of research, described below, came to similar conclusions:

- **ATD** (*Asynchronous Time Division*);
- **FPS** (*Fast Packet Switching*).

1.1.1   The ATD technique

This technique used very short fixed-length packets (about 16 bytes) with a header limited to three bytes containing a label for a virtual circuit type routing. The use of short packets guarantees, as in the case of circuit switching, a brief and relatively constant delay, which means that, for example, voice signals can be transferred without using echo cancellers.

This ATD technique was mainly promoted by European organizations (manufacturers, operators, the RACE project) in the context of studies and models based, for the most part, on isochronous flow transfer (voice and video). Furthermore, these projects made no assumptions about a particular transmission infrastructure. In particular, the aim of research by CNET at Lannion was to provide high speed circuits for video communication in a residential context, as well as data transmission and high quality sound. The Prelude experimental network, based on a basic switching matrix with 16 incoming lines and 16 outgoing lines working at 280 Mbits/s, was used to evaluate the soundness of the chosen approach: a suitable packet mode can carry traffic with differing characteristics, including isochronous flows.

In their first phase, the Bigfon and Berkom experimental networks in Germany were based on a circuit switching technique. However, the growing consensus around ATD caused the Deutsche Bundespost to delay installing its public broadband network and, in 1988, Siemens became the first manufacturer to install an experimental exchange, for Berkom, based on these principles.

1.1.2   The FPS technique

At the same time, research was being undertaken by organizations such as AT&T Bell Labs, Network Systems, Bellcore, GTE Labs, and IBM (PARIS experimental network), with the main aim of transmitting computer data efficiently at very high speeds. These studies were concomitant with the development of the **SONET** (*Synchronous Optical NETwork*) standard for networks based on fibre optics, which were beginning to be installed in the USA.

The term Fast Packet Switching, popularized by J. Turner, covers most of these projects. They were based on short packets (about 100 bytes), either of fixed length (Bellcore) or variable length (AT&T, IBM). Quite a large header (about 5 bytes) contained, along with the label, binary elements used to distinguish between different levels of priority. The performance they were aiming for meant that the traditional packet switching protocols had to be simplified and the switching functions carried out by hardware components.

1.1.3   Fast packet switching

The two avenues of research described above have important characteristics in common:

- The network access supports all types of traffic: voice, data, fixed and moving images.

- The transfer mode to the access is flexible and allows for dynamic allocation of the bandwidth according to the immediate needs of the user system.

- Statistical multiplexing of the high speed digital links is suitable for bursty traffic. For the user, it results in lower costs while for the network provider, it means the use of links can be optimized. Individual end-to-end users may use a significant proportion, or even the whole, of the link's capacity for limited periods.

- Asynchronous transfer is particularly adapted to variable speed coding. In this context, we should note that even though they have traditionally been transmitted as continuous flows, voice and video are, by nature, bursty. In the case of voice, an activity detection mechanism can be used to block the coder when the sound source is silent; by compressing the vocal signal during activity periods we get an average flow rate of 10kbits/s. Similarly, a video source is extremely bursty: when movements in the image are slight, there is little difference between successive images; the new information is limited and can be transmitted infrequently, in the form of packets. Conversely, if there is a rapid movement or a complete change of image, the new information increases considerably, and the source then transmits a burst of packets at a much higher rate. Obviously, this form of coding optimizes the use of the transmission lines, without complicating the operation of the source.

- The transfer mode is unique. Even the most enthusiastic proponents of circuit switching did not manage to propose it as the sole switching technique, and there were several hybrid approaches: circuit switching for continuous flows, packet switching for bursty traffic. The universality of the proposed transfer mode is a most important advantage.

All these common characteristics were recognized by the packet switching lobby, but some questions still had to be resolved: the size of packets, fixed or variable length, and so on. Furthermore, the use of circuit switching had not been excluded. It was within the CCITT that these crucial questions were resolved.

1.1.4 The role of the CCITT

In June 1985, CCITT Study Group XVIII formed a *BroadBand Task Group* (**BBTG**) responsible for looking at matters concerning the user interface of broadband ISDN.

Roughly speaking, the two propositions illustrated in Figure 1.1 were in competition for international standardization:

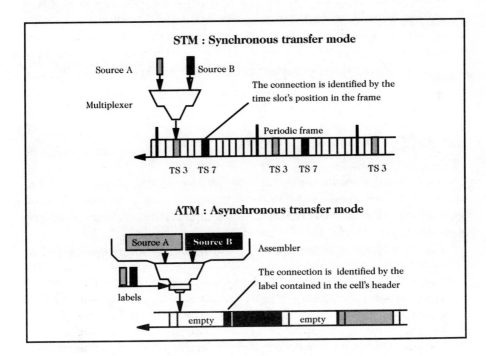

Figure 1.1 Comparison between synchronous and asynchronous transfer modes

- A synchronous approach, called **STM** (*Synchronous Transfer Mode*) by the CCITT, based on rapid circuit switching. On a multiplexed link, an STM channel is identified in a frame by the position of the time slots assigned to it. Fixed speed channels were proposed: narrow band ISDN channels and others which could be used for transmitting video signals and high quality sound. As the **SDH** (*Synchronous Digital Hierarchy*) standard was being adopted at the same time, some of the channels proposed could be carried in the payload of future synchronous transmission systems. However, an interface constructed on a fixed channel structure lacks flexibility: it freezes the characteristics of the services it carries; these services may vary from one country to another, from one client to another, and, above all, they may well change over time.

- An asynchronous approach, proposed by both the supporters of ATD and those of *Fast Packet Switching*. The CCITT named it **ATM** (*Asynchronous Transfer Mode*), even though the size of the packets (later called cells) had not been decided. The ATM approach does not require a framed transmission system; a connection is identified by the *label* contained in the cell's header. Thus, several connections can be multiplexed at the same time on a '*labelled multiplex*' link. The use of unframed media is made possible by a cell self-delineation mechanism: the system is then called 'pure ATM', referred to these days as 'cell-based systems' (see page 31). Naturally, ATM flows can be carried by framed transmission systems, in particular in SDH containers (see page 29).

1.1.5. The ATM compromise

The ATM transfer mode, which resulted from the studies mentioned above, combines the advantages of previous techniques. Figure 1.2 summarizes the main characteristics of the traditional switching methods (circuit mode and packet mode).

The ATM transfer mode preserves the following advantages of circuit mode:

- The network transmits the cell's *payload* in a totally **transparent** way, just like the eight bits in a time slot.

- The payload has a **fixed length**, just like a time slot's byte, which means that relatively simple high-performance switching mechanisms can be designed.

- The payload is **short**. This characteristic means that a circuit can be emulated, while at the same time guaranteeing a jitter compatible with the constraints imposed by voice or moving image transmission.

Constraints	Circuit switching (ISDN)	Packet switching (X.25)	Cell switching (ATM)
Real time	Yes	No	Yes
Transparency	Yes	No	Yes
End-to-end protocol	Yes	No	Yes
Variable bit rate	No	Yes	Yes
Statistical multiplexing	No	Yes	Yes

Figure 1.2   Criteria for choosing cell switching

Other advantages are preserved from packet mode:

- The source and the network are not tied by the necessity of transmitting and receiving a quantity of information synchronously with a frame and during a time slot assigned to the connection involved. The exchange with the network is **asynchronous** and the source alone is responsible for its bit rate, within the limits of the contract defined at the start of the communication (*bandwidth on demand*).

- In order to optimize use of the network, connections can be **statistically multiplexed**, on condition that the quality of service required for each of them allows it.

- Routing by **labels** opens the door to numerous possibilities, such as: broadcasting, setting up user groups, dividing the network into a hierarchy of link sets and virtual channels.

As shown in Figure 1.3, ATM combines the simplicity of circuit switching with the flexibility of packet switching.

The 48-byte size of the ATM cell's payload is the result of a compromise: during a CCITT meeting in Geneva, the representatives of the USA and a few other countries recommended a 64-byte data field, whereas the European countries favoured a 32-byte field. As there was no irrefutable technical consensus on the matter, the compromise decision was to adopt the halfway position between the two propositions.

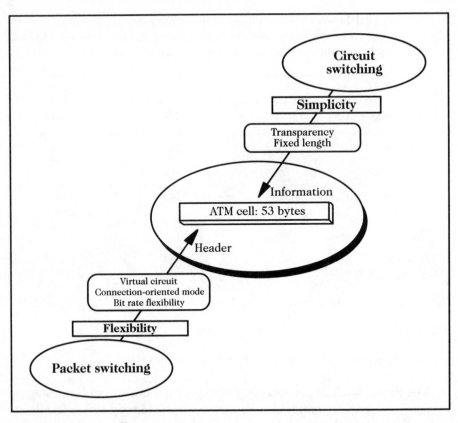

Figure 1.3   The position of cell relay

While on this subject we should note that when transmitting a digital telephone signal, assembly into cells leads to a delay of 6 ms (48 bytes transmitted at 64 kbits/s), or the equivalent of the propagation time over a distance of more than 1000 km. In medium size countries (for example, European countries), this additional delay may require the installation of echo cancellation systems, whereas nowadays these are only required for international connections.

1.2   The development of telecommunications

The ATM concept was only able to take shape and gain the consent of the majority so rapidly because its roots lie deep in general developments in the telecommunications domain. The choices made were not an upset, but rather an integration of the progress made in existing techniques; in the long term, this should lead to the unification of the transfer modes used by all the devices that belong to the communication media (terminals, local area networks, wide area networks, and so on).

The telecommunications world is constantly developing, with each new technique usually building on the preceding ones. Thus, the digital multiplex hierarchy is based on frequency division multiplexing and the frame relay technique is an improvement on packet switching; similarly, narrow band ISDN can be seen as the final standardization of a telecommunications infrastructure which has constantly been modernizing itself.

The growth in demand for professional communications has led to two types of network:

- the dedicated public networks (X.25, for example);
- private company networks, built using leased lines.

If we followed this logic, we would end up with a network for each service in the public domain and one for each application in the private domain, with the obvious losses of economies of scale. The availability of a multi-service network technology can only be welcomed, both in the public and private domains.

1.2.1 Technological features

The introduction of **fibre optics** into public and private network infrastructures is becoming widespread. They enable interconnected workstations to operate remotely with very short response times, at the same bit rates and with the same quality as on a computer bus.

This has caused a switchover in the respective roles of the network and the computer. For a long time, communication between processing units was limited by networks which only provided relatively low bit rates. Networks with fibre optics provide a bandwidth equal, if not superior, to that of the processing units' internal buses or input/output channels. The computer and its peripherals are no longer restricted to a single computer room, the era of distributed processing and the client–server model has dawned.

Though the bandwidth made available by fibre optics is large, it is not infinite and will always be relatively expensive once large distances have to be taken into consideration. Furthermore, bandwidth needs continue to increase, given, amongst other things, the growing improvement in quality required by terminal equipment (screen size, number of pixels per image, number of colours) and the introduction of moving images. For all these reasons, data compression techniques are necessary.

Another important aspect is the generalization of **digital techniques** in the transfer mode as well as the processing and the storing of data. Allied to technological advances in very large-scale integrated (VLSI) circuits, memories and signal processors, these techniques enable important progress to be made, in terms of both functions and costs.

Thus, these digital techniques have now made it possible to implement **fast packet switching**, using hardware components, on condition that it is relatively simple and only allows a few options. In order to simplify the associated protocols, the more complex functions (segmentation, error handling, flow control, and so on) are offloaded onto the terminal devices, whose capacities for low-cost processing are considerable.

Display techniques derived from televisual processes are increasingly used on workstations: whereas in the past they were limited to managing text, spreadsheets or still images, they are slowly allowing multimedia communication (face-to-face conversation via video windows, sound, text, data transfer, and so on). We should note that progress in data compression means that nowadays the bit rate necessary for a high definition television type video image is only 30 Mbits/s, and for VHS quality moving images only 1.5 Mbits/s.

1.2.2   Planned applications

Tomorrow's network must support the applications we know today, those that we are planning and, even more importantly, those that we have not even imagined. As Figure 1.4 shows, its switching mode must accommodate a large variety of bit rates (from several kbits/s to several Mbits/s), constant or bursty flows and different qualities of service (more or less sensitive to variations in delay or to error rates).

In the business world, the main aim is to provide the same communication possibilities to all users, wherever they are located geographically. Applications, which today are restricted to local area networks, may thus become available remotely: high speed data transfer, graphic applications, computer-aided design, and so on. Rapid access to remote databases or servers allows processing to be distributed. In a way, it is the network, with its distributed servers, that is becoming the company's computer, and thus responsible for response time and quality of service constraints.

In the world of professional applications, there are specific needs awaiting the installation of appropriate networks in order to become truly available over a wide area: medical imaging with the possibility of immediate annotation, teleconferencing with moving images, remote editing and training, and many more.

It is noticeable that most pilot projects (for example, the European RACE projects) involve professional applications.

In the domestic area, the target applications are mainly concerned with entertainment: high quality television pictures, amongst others, but also television on request. For this last application, the means for consulting a list of films and performing the classic operations of a local video recorder remotely must be made available. In the years from 1980 to 1985, it was the common belief that the main commercial force behind the success of a broadband network in the residential market would be entertainment. Various difficulties, such as installation of fibre optics that reach homes in the distribution network and competition from other technologies, such as cable and satellite, have pushed that perspective back into the 2000s.

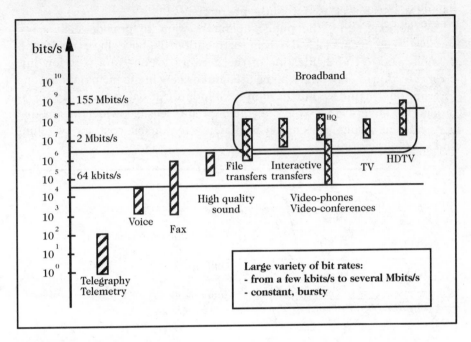

Figure 1.4 The variety of bit rates that need to be supported for the different applications

This explains why, faced with a constantly changing competitive market and the need to find new sources of revenue, network operators target the professional market first, and principally the interconnection of local area networks. Paradoxically, the installation of a high speed network based on fast packet switching relocates the added value to the network's periphery, in the terminals connected to it, which does not necessarily lead to it being adopted rapidly.

The existence of high capacity digital trunks is essential for all the applications envisaged, whether professional or domestic, both to support the **large flows** generated by the information sources and to guarantee a satisfactory **response time**.

1.2.3 Existing services

Existing services, based on circuit or packet techniques, generally use dedicated networks which are well suited to traditional applications.

However, they are only partially satisfactory for the new applications mentioned above, because the latter are multi-service and generate large and bursty flows. Businesses that have to install such applications today have to create private networks, whose backbone is made up of 2.048 or 34.368 Mbits/s lines leased from the operators.

In the long term, the public operators want to provide high speed services. The technological advances mentioned above have made this possible: end-to-end digitization of the network leading to a very low line error rate, due to fibre optics being used intensively in the main national and international trunks. Furthermore, standardization makes the mass production of very large-scale integrated circuits feasible, which means that very efficient technologies are available, at a reasonable cost, for switching and signal processing.

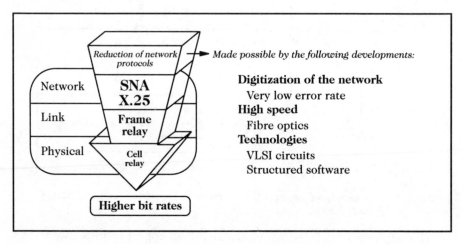

Figure 1.5   Changes in information transfer technologies

In order to take advantage of these technological advances, the architecture of the communication protocols needs to be revised. In particular, the significant reduction in the error rates of transmission systems means that the protocols in the network nodes can be reduced, and the network nodes can be simplified so that they can handle higher bit rates (see Figure 1.5).

1.2.4   Constraints

The objective is to define a single transfer mode, but that mode must be able to satisfy all the constraints imposed by the applications described above. It is not possible to establish a hierarchy of these constraints; they are all equally critical and their relative importance is only a factor of the particular application.

Thus, multimedia applications present numerous constraints which are not necessarily independent (for example, the image and the sound must be transmitted with similar characteristics). Furthermore, those constraints may change during a single connection.

Real time

Voice transmission, along with video, is the most common example of an application with real-time requirements: every 125 µs, a sound signal sample is transmitted in the form of a byte and this must be reconstituted on reception with the same regularity, no matter what happens during transmission. Traditionally, circuit switching provides an isochronous service which satisfies these requirements. However, **circuit emulation** can be achieved by a packet type technique, on condition that the global delay and its variations are limited: the use of short fixed-length packets favours such an approach.

Conventional local area networks (CSMA/CD bus, token ring, **FDDI** (*Fibre Distributed Data Interface*) network) do not guarantee the required real-time characteristics, especially when the network is heavily loaded. FDDI-II extends the FDDI protocol functions in order to respond to these requirements by reserving channels (**WBC**, *WideBand Channels*) for use by isochronous traffic. Improvements to other local area networks are also being studied (for example, the 100 Mbits/s Ethernet network).

Bit rate

A multi-service network must support a large variety of bit rates; furthermore, these may be bursty or unsymmetrical. On the other hand, the characteristics of a given service and the corresponding bit rate cannot be set once and for all; the speed may vary over time, given the advances made in compression algorithms and the availability of very fast signal processors. Finally, predicting the characteristics of future services is a risky business. Therefore, a multi-service network must be flexible enough to adapt to all sorts of bit rates, if it is to last.

Quality of service

The required quality of service varies according to the application. Some are more tolerant than others of disturbances in the flow of information. A common transfer mode must therefore be reasonably accommodating towards these differences; 'reasonably' means that a single service cannot be perfect; an adaptation function that can compensate for the network's imperfections must be inserted near the application.

The first supporters of ATM, defined by the CCITT as the target technology for the future broadband ISDN, were the public network operators and their traditional suppliers. However, around 1991, ATM attracted the attention of the manufacturers of the interconnection devices (concentrators, bridges, routers) and packet switches used in private networks, along with, more recently, the manufacturers of workstations and personal computers, and finally, of software.

Therefore, it is probable that the first ATM products will be put on the market in the private domain, as a supplement to traditional local area network techniques, or even in direct competition with them.

In the longer term, it is possible that this transfer mode will be used end to end between two workstations linked by local area networks or private ATM switching units, which are themselves connected by a public broadband ATM network.

In the following chapter, we present the technical characteristics of ATM, not only as they are described in the CCITT recommendations, but also in the documents approved and published by the ATM Forum (see page 80), a manufacturers' association created in 1991 which now includes some 500 representatives.

2

Cell relay

2.1   Principles

ATM is both a switching and a multiplexing technique, and also a transmission technique. It is a variation on packet switching, in so far as it only
uses short fixed-length packets called **cells**. Cell handling by an ATM
switching unit is limited to analysing the label (part of the header, similar to
a logical channel number) so that the cell can be routed to the appropriate
output queue. The more complex functions, such as error handling and flow
control, are not carried out by the ATM network, but left to the user
systems.

These particular features furnish a reasonable solution to the problems
posed by the simultaneous constraints of traffic as diverse as voice, moving
images and all types of data. Because it is so flexible, ATM can eventually
integrate all services onto a common access to a single network.

Cell switching is located between the transmission functions and those
concerned with adapting the information flow to the cell format. This gives
us a three-layer model (see Figure 2.1):

- the **ATM** layer, responsible for multiplexing and switching the cells;
- the physical layer, which adapts them to the transmission environment;
- the **AAL** layer (*ATM Adaptation Layer*), which adapts the information flows to the cells' structure.

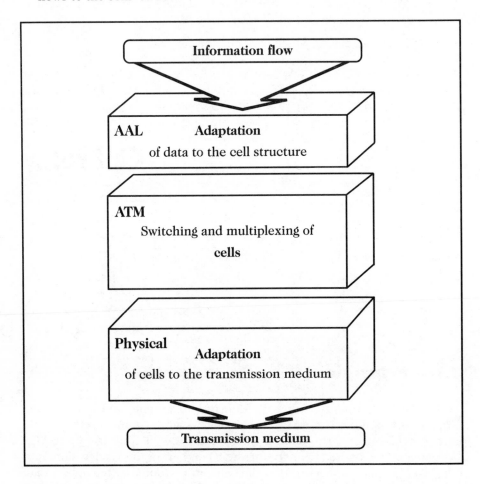

Figure 2.1   Architectural model for cell relay

We will discuss these three layers starting with the central one (the cell), then enlarging the discussion to take in the transmission environment and ending with the adaptation of the information flows.

We should note that cell relay is used not only by ATM technology but also by **DQDB** (*Distributed Queue Dual Bus*) technology, adopted by the IEEE as the data transfer and medium access technique for metropolitan area networks.

2.2   ATM layer functions

A cell is 53 bytes long and contains two main fields (see Figure 2.2):

- a header (5 bytes), whose main role is to identify the cells that belong to the same connection and allow them to be routed,

- a data field (48 bytes), which contains the payload.

The cells used at the broadband subscriber access (**UNI**, *User Network Interface*) have a slightly different header from those used at the interface between networks (**NNI**, *Network Node Interface*).

The ATM cell header used at the interface between the user and the network (UNI cell) contains the following fields:

- a flow control field (**GFC**, *Generic Flow Control*), whose definition has not yet been finalized. It is used to regulate priorities and access contentions between several terminals (**point-to-multipoint** configuration, see page 70). Another proposed use for this field, in the context of local ATM networks, is for flow control and preventing congestion;

- three bytes use for the logical identifier (VPI and VCI, see page 19);

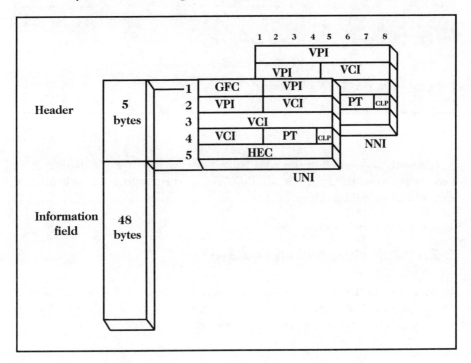

Figure 2.2   ATM cell structure

- three **PTI** (*Payload Type Identification*) bits used to describe the type of payload (user data or network service message, see Figure 2.3). In the first case, the last two bits provide a congestion indicator, as well as the type of data unit, which is interpreted by the upper layers. This type is transmitted to the adaptation layer (AAL) by the ATM layer, and can be seen as an extension of the adaptation functions: it is used by the AAL type 5 function to indicate the last cell in a segmentation operation (see page 42);

- one **CLP** (*Cell Loss Priority*) bit, whose role is specified on page 21;

- one **HEC** (*Header Error Control*) byte for detecting errors and correcting a simple error involving the header. The handling of this byte, described on page 25, is the responsibility of the physical layer.

	Type of flow	Congestion indicator	Type of data unit
000	0 User	0 No congestion	0 Type 0 unit
001	0 User	0 No congestion	1 Type 1 unit
010	0 User	1 Congestion encountered	0 Type 0 unit
011	0 User	1 Congestion encountered	1 Type 1 unit
100	1 Network	0 Maintenance (segment by segment)	
101	1 Network	0 Maintenance (end to end)	
110	1 Network	1 Network resources management	
111	1 Network	1 Reserved	

Figure 2.3   Payload Type Indicator coding (PTI)

The only difference in the ATM cell header used between networks (NNI cell) is that the GFC field is missing. The corresponding bits are used to extend the logical identifier field.

2.2.1 Principle of cell routing

Because the ATM service is connection-oriented, routing tables are required in the network switching units. Each cell is set on its route by the intermediate switching units, which associate its identifier with a destination, as shown in Figure 2.4.

As in the case of packet switching or frame relay, the logical identifier only has a local meaning. In this case it is made up of two fields (see Figure 2.2, page 17):

- a group identifier or **VPI** (*Virtual Path Identifier*): it is 8 bits long in a UNI cell and 12 bits long in an NNI cell;

- an identifier of the element in the group or **VCI** (*Virtual Channel Identifier*) which is 16 bits long.

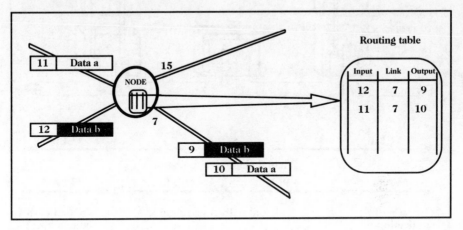

Figure 2.4   Principle of cell routing

A pair composed of a virtual path (VP) and a virtual channel (VC) is the equivalent of a virtual circuit in packet switching or a **virtual link** in frame relay. The notion of a virtual path is used by the network manager to organize and manage the transmission resources, using permanent or semi-permanent virtual links.

As indicated in figure 2.5, a route is made up of two types of connection: a **virtual path connection** and a **virtual channel connection**. Each connection is made up of a concatenation of virtual channels and paths. The hierarchy of identifiers (VPI, VCI) allows for the development of two types of switching units:

- ATM virtual path switching units, usually called **VP cross-connects** (*ATM Digital Cross-Connects* or *ATM DCC*), which only use the virtual path identifier (VPI) to forward the data along the route. They are controlled by the network management units;

- ATM virtual channel switching units, which take both identifiers into account (VPI and VCI). These are mainly network access exchanges operated on a call-by-call basis by call handling mechanisms.

A VP cross-connect is used to route all the virtual channels belonging to the same path as a block. These cross-connects can be used to configure leased line networks, to provide stand-by routes, to make up the interconnection between switching nodes in a connectionless service, and so on.

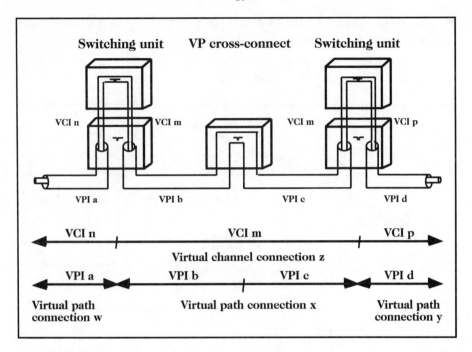

Figure 2.5 Cell relay: the dual routing mechanism

Cells are assigned to a connection according to the source's activity and the network availability. There are two modes for assigning connections:

- permanent assignment or **virtual permanent connection**, which is the result of a service contract between the network operator and the user;

- assignment on request, call by call, or **switched virtual connection**, which requires a signalling protocol between the user terminal and the network access switching unit.

This signalling protocol is itself carried on a separate virtual connection which, like any other virtual connection, can be assigned to the signalling activity permanently or on request (call by call). In the latter case, signalling virtual connection set-up makes use of a special procedure, called **metasignalling**. The protocols necessary for assigning virtual connections on request, call by call, are discussed on page 70.

2.2.2 Protection against congestion

Terminal devices are responsible for the flows they generate, in accordance with a contract between the user and the network. This **traffic contract** describes the characteristics of the source's traffic, such as its average bit rate, its maximum bit rate, and the type and duration of bursts (burstiness), for each connection. It also defines the quality of service attributes associated with the connection, in particular the cell loss probability and the cell jitter and delay. These characteristics can be defined when the subscription is taken out or negotiated call by call, which requires a signalling procedure (see page 68).

The cell loss priority (CLP) bit in each cell's header is used in the congestion protection mechanisms. Generally, this bit is controlled by the source, which determines the relative importance of the data carried in each cell.

An example of a possible use is in the multirate coding of video: the CLP bit is set to 1 in cells that are carrying less important information. If the network becomes congested, these cells are discarded first, leading to a loss of image quality, which is less important than a loss of transmission.

Protection against congestion calls on a set of mechanisms which are brought into play during different phases of the connection:

Admission control

The first preventive measure is a **connection admission control** for new connections. Given the traffic characteristics (illustrated in Figure 2.6), the network must decide if it has the necessary resources available to be able to guarantee the quality of service requested by the user, and then reserve those resources for the duration of the connection:

- If the quality of service required is very demanding, the bandwidth reserved must be equal to the source's maximum bit rate (**M**), also called the **peak bit rate**. Thus, the network can guarantee to route all the bursts of information to their destination within a guaranteed time limit and with a practically zero probability of cell loss.

- If the quality of service is less stringent, in terms of delay variation and loss of data, the network can take statistical probabilities into account and only reserve the bandwidth equal to the **sustainable rate** for the connection. This bit rate (**S**) is in between the source's average bit rate (**m**) and its maximum bit rate (**M**); the more long bursts the traffic contains, the nearer it will be to the maximum bit rate.

Spacing and rate policing

Once the connection has been set up, the source implements a spacing mechanism (*source shaping*) when transmitting information, in order to respect its access contract.

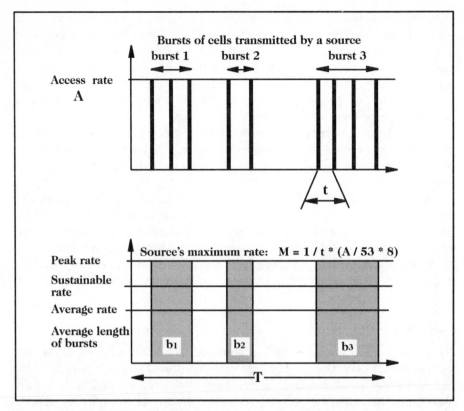

Figure 2.6   Characteristics of the bit rate of a source of traffic

We should note that in the case of an access to a network using circuit mode, also called **STM**, the source can only use the bit rate corresponding to the time slots assigned to it when the connection is established; the network only takes into account the data contained in those time slots, and therefore the bit rate accepted is **calibrated** by construction. In contrast, when accessing a network using ATM, there is nothing to stop the source offering traffic greater than that specified in its contract on the virtual channel assigned to it, either intentionally or following an equipment failure. Therefore, the network must carry out the **calibration** itself, by controlling and regulating the bit rate offered on the virtual channel in accordance with the contract. It is essential that the network protects itself against such situations or it will not be able to guarantee the quality of service offered to the connections because there will be overflows of the queues in the switching units.

Therefore, **rate policing** is implemented at the network access. It is beyond the scope of this book to discuss the control mechanisms in detail, as they are complicated and still under discussion. For each connection, they combine the following functions:

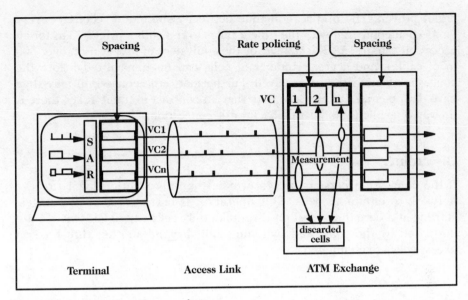

Figure 2.7 Spacing and rate policing

- a **measurement** of the bit rate offered, which usually uses *leaky bucket* type algorithms whose parameters depend on the quality of service associated with the connection;

- a **control**, which is used to eliminate cells in excess of the contract, or to reduce their level of priority by one. This last method goes by the name of *violation tagging*.

Spacing is carried out on the cells before they are fed onto the network, according to the bandwidth reserved for the connection involved (see Figure 2.7).

These rate policing and spacing functions are implemented separately on the priority cells (CLP = 0) and on all the cells related to the connection (CLP = 0 and CLP = 1).

Congestion notification

In spite of these precautions taken at the interfaces to the network, a state of congestion can temporarily occur in a switching unit because of the statistical accumulation of bursts of cells belonging to different connections. Such congestion is generally detected by an overflow of a threshold in the switching unit's queues.

An **EFCN** (*Explicit Forward Congestion Notification*) may then be activated in the cells that have passed through the congested switching unit. This congestion notification is provided by the second bit of the cell header's PTI field (see page 18). Given the projected bit rates for high speed networks such as broadband ISDN (see page 61), the effectiveness of such a mechanism is not proven. The propagation time between source and receiver is very long, when compared with the time it takes to transmit a cell (2.73 µs for an access bit rate of 155.520 Mbits/s, or the equivalent of propagation over 500 m of cable), and a great number of cells can be transmitted before the congestion notification is received. Furthermore, the congestion may then have disappeared. We can also note that, in contrast to frame relay, there is no way of explicitly indicating backwards congestion.

Discarding

If the congestion persists or gets worse, the only solution left is for the network to eliminate cells. This operation is carried out in two stages: starting at a certain congestion threshold, only cells whose CLP bit = 1 are destroyed by the congested switching unit; beyond another threshold all excess cells are eliminated.

2.2.3   Multiplexing information flows

Cell relay is not only a switching technique, but also a multiplexing technique.

The cells are generated on demand, depending on the source's bit rate. The data items are first adjusted to the size of the payload and the connection's header added. This cell generation process is solely governed by the source's own bit rate, and is not linked to the characteristics of the underlying transmission medium (bit rate, any delineation pattern, and so on). This is why the technology is called **asynchronous transfer**, as opposed to circuit switching and multiplexing: in this latter mode (synchronous transfer), the source must provide a data item for each frame, usually every 125 µs, in order to fill the time slot it has been allocated.

The multiplexing of cells transmitted by different sources that share the same access link is similar to the multiplexing of packets belonging to different virtual circuits in packet switching. The discontinuous flow of cells resulting from the multiplexing of several connections is transmitted to the physical layer.

2.3   Functions of the physical layer

One result of the functional layer structure is that the constraints imposed on the physical layer by the ATM layer are very limited. The flow of cells generated by the ATM layer can be carried in the payload of practically any digital transmission system, which means it can be adapted to any present or future transmission system.

The physical layer can be divided into two sublayers, which provide the main functions listed:

- the convergence sublayer handles bit rate adaptation, header protection, cell delineation and adaptation to the physical medium's structure;

- the physical medium sublayer is responsible for coding, decoding, scrambling and adaptation to the medium.

2.3.1 Rate adaptation

Usually, the bit rate of the flow of multiplexed cells provided by the ATM layer is not equal to the working bit rate of the physical access link. Rate adaptation, often called **stuffing** or **justifying**, is necessary. The different ways of carrying out this adaptation can be grouped into three main techniques, the third of which is really a combination of the first two:

- In order to generate a continuous flow of cells, empty cells are inserted into the flow. In the case of a framed transmission system, the resulting flow then corresponds to the transmission link's payload (for example, SDH synchronous frames), whereas, if the transmission link is 'cell based', it is equal to the total bit rate of the link. This insertion method has been retained by the CCITT for broadband ISDN.

- Conversely, the flow of cells can remain discontinuous: this type of flow is mainly found in ATM local area networks which have yet to be standardized. As the time interval between cells may be of any length, stuffing characters (*idle* symbols) can be inserted to adapt the bit rate. For example, this technique is used for ATM transmission on an infrastructure using the FDDI physical layer at 100 Mbits/s (see page 84) .

- A combination of the two previous methods consists in grouping a constant number of cells in blocks, which may be padded with empty cells. The difference between these blocks and the bit rate may be filled by a variable number of stuffing bytes, so as to guarantee a strict sequence of blocks, one every 125 µs: this last method is used for ATM transmission on plesiochronous links, **PDH** (*Plesiochronous Digital Hierarchy*).

2.3.2 Header protection by the HEC

As cell routing is based on the VPI and VCI fields, they must be protected because, if there is an error, routing becomes impossible. The HEC provides this protection. Generally, transmission errors are independent from each other, especially in an optical network: they mostly cause isolated errors, which can be corrected relatively simply. In the case of error bursts (due, for example, to configuration modification operations on a network made up of redundant links), correction is not allowed and faulty cells found during that period are discarded. In any case, whether the error is isolated or grouped, if it exceeds the HEC (header error control) field's correction capacity, the cell will be destroyed.

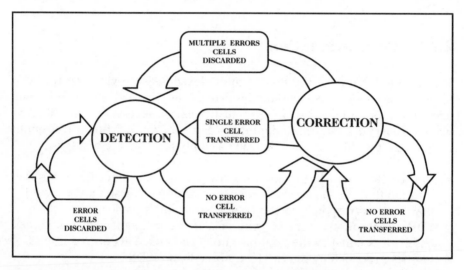

Figure 2.8   Error detection and correction using the HEC field

The receiver has a **correction** mode and a **detection** mode for the header protection mechanism:

- In correction mode, which is the normal operating mode, cells whose HEC shows no error syndrome are passed to the higher layers; cells whose HEC shows a single error are passed after the faulty header has been corrected, whereas those with multiple errors are destroyed.

- The detection of an invalid HEC (single or multiple errors) causes a change to detection mode, in which all the cells whose HEC is faulty are destroyed. Conversely, the detection of a cell with a correct HEC causes a return to correction mode.

Figure 2.8 illustrates this two-mode procedure, which is used to protect the receiver as far as possible against bursts of errors: when one error is found, the receiver assumes it is the start of a burst and changes to detection mode, in order to avoid making unnecessary corrections. If this hypothesis is proved false when the next cell is received, it returns to correction mode.

Mathematically, the HEC's value for any given header is derived by applying the following procedure:

- The 32 bits of the header's first four bytes are used as the coefficients of a 31- degree polynomial $M(x)$ (the first bit corresponds to term x^{31} and the last to term x^0) .

- The polynomial $M(x)$ is multiplied by x^8 then divided (modulo 2) by a generator polynomial $G(x) = x^8 + x^2 + x + 1$;

- The polynomial $C(x) = x^6 + x^4 + x^2 + 1$ is added (modulo 2) to the remainder of the division, thus producing a polynomial $R(x)$ whose coefficients form the 8-bit sequence of the HEC (fifth byte in the header).

The byte thus generated provides a Hamming distance of four, a property which allows all single bit errors to be corrected (only one bit in error) as well as the detection of all two-bit errors.

2.3.3   Cell delineation

When cells are received, their limits have to be identified. This delineation function can be carried out in various ways, depending on the technique used for adapting the bit rate.

Adaptation by continuous flow of cells

In the case of a continuous flow of cells, a delineation function, independent of the transmission system, has been defined. It is based on the detection of the cell header's HEC field. Use of a scrambler improves security and robustness (see page 31).

Cell delineation is based on the use of the HEC field which protects the first four bytes of the header. This method does not rely on any special delineation pattern, as using the HEC allows self-delineation of the ATM cells.

The limits of a cell in a continuous digital flow are detected by determining the byte where the HEC coding rules are proven true (see above). This self-delineation procedure is based on the finite state diagram shown in Figure 2.9.

In the **search** for cell limits state, the mechanism checks, bit by bit, if the HEC coding rules apply to the assumed header. On detecting the first cell limit determined by receiving a valid HEC, the mechanism changes to the **pre-synchronisation** state. In this state, the mechanism continues to check that the HEC coding rules apply to the bytes assumed to contain an HEC.

When *delta* consecutive valid HECs are detected, the change to the **synchronization** state is authorized, whereas the detection of an invalid HEC causes a return to the search state. In the synchronization state, the mechanism continues to check the HECs: when *alpha* consecutive invalid HECs are detected, there is a return to the search state.

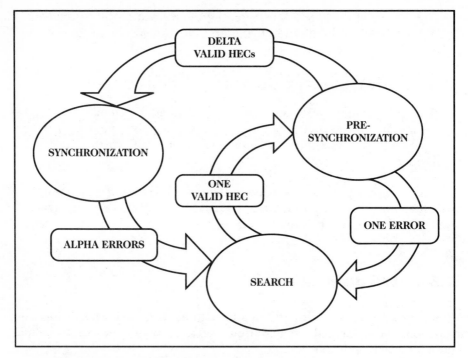

Figure 2.9   Principle of ATM cell delineation

The larger the number of consecutive invalid HECs necessary in order to consider delineation lost, *alpha*, the smaller the probability of losing delineation when there is a transmission error. But the larger the *alpha*, the longer it takes to detect a loss of delineation.

The probability of incorrect delineation diminishes with large values of *delta*, the number of consecutive valid HECs necessary in order to consider the delineation acquired. However, the larger the *delta*, the longer the delineation acquisition time.

Two sets of values have been proposed according to the type of physical medium:

* 7 for *alpha* and 6 for *delta* for synchronous transmission systems;
* 7 for *alpha* and 8 for *delta* for cell-based transmission systems.

For error rates of 10^{-6} bits, the time between two losses of delineation is larger than 10^{30} cells.

Other rate adaptation techniques

When rate adaptation is not based on the generation of a continuous flow of cells, the delineation technique which uses HEC field detection is not necessarily possible. In this case, a delineation pattern must be provided for each cell, in the form of bytes or symbols. Some specific examples are described in the next section.

2.3.4   Adaptation to the transmission systems

Once the problems of bit rate adaptation and cell delineation have been resolved, the digital flows have to be fed into the transmission system, whether framed or not.

For framed transmission systems, two cases of *mapping* a continuous flow of cells into the payload need to be considered:

* using a synchronous transmission medium (SDH);

* using a plesiochronous transmission medium (PDH).

Adaptation to synchronous transmission

In the case of an SDH synchronous transmission, the adaptation takes place at path level. CCITT Recommendation I.432 specifies the mapping for STM-1 frames at 155.520 Mbits/s (as well as STM-4 frames at 622.080 Mbits/s). The

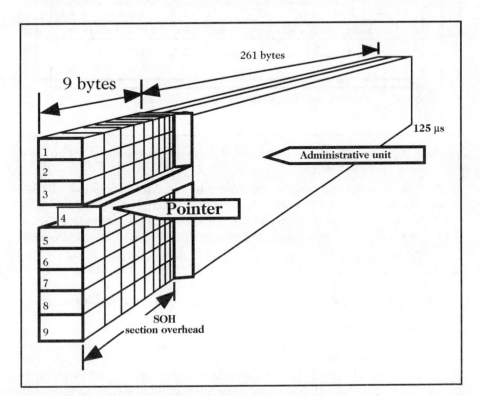

Figure 2.10   Structure of the STM-1 synchronous frame

STM-1 synchronous frame provides a capacity of 2430 bytes every 125 µs (155 520 kbits/s). These 2430 bytes are arranged in 270 columns and 9 rows and are transmitted row by row. The first nine rows (81 bytes) do not carry data and are an **overhead**, used to delineate and manage the frame. Figure 2.10 shows the structure of an STM-1 synchronous frame.

The remaining 2349 bytes form a fourth-order virtual container, VC-4, which in turn is made up of a column (9 bytes) that contains the **POH** (*Path OverHead*) and the container itself, and provides a transmission capacity of 2 340 bytes every 125 µs (149 760 kbits/s). The path overhead is used for management functions (parity check on the path, type of payload, continuity check on the path, and so on). Byte C2 (type of payload = ATM) is specific to the mapping of ATM cells into a C-4 container.

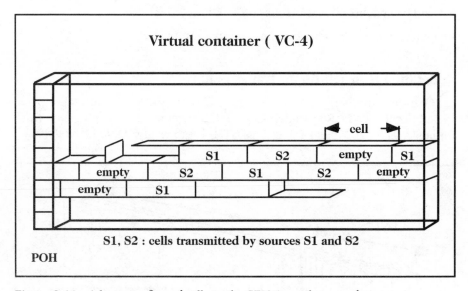

Figure 2.11   Adapting a flow of cells to the STM-1 synchronous frame

A whole number of 53-byte cells cannot be fitted into a payload of 2340 bytes. Furthermore, the flow of cells is mapped continuously into the C-4 container, so that some of them overlap onto the adjacent frame (see Figure 2.11). In the case of this type of mapping, cell delineation is based on the HEC field.

Adaptation to plesiochronous transmission (Recommendation G.804)

In the case of a plesiochronous transmission, the cells can be grouped in a periodic frame, which also includes maintenance functions. The associated protocol, **PLCP** (Physical Layer Convergence Protocol), is derived from those defined by ETSI for IEEE standard 802.6, which is used for metropolitan area networks. It involves the 44 736 kbits/s PDH layer. Four bytes are added to each cell mapped into the transmission payload; the first two provide a delineation pattern, the third the order number of the cell in the 125 µs frame, and the fourth is reserved for management functions similar to those provided by the path overhead (POH) in the synchronous digital hierarchy (SDH). The overhead associated with this technique is quite large and another method consists in simply mapping the cells into the payload of a PDH frame. For example, using this technique, 10 cells can be mapped into a 34 368 kbits/s frame, the HEC field being used for delineation.

Adaptation to an unframed transmission system

When the transmission system is unframed, other techniques must be used. The examples given below involve mapping cells onto local area network systems and are based on studies being carried out in the context of the ATM Forum (see page 80).

In the case of ATM transmission at 100 Mbits/s using 4B/5B coding and the physical media developed for FDDI networks, the start of each cell is identified by a pair of symbols 'TT', whereas the pair of symbols 'JK' is used for stuffing between cells; this 100 Mbits/s interface is often called the 'TAXI interface' (*Transparent Asynchronous Xmitter-receiver Interface*) after the integrated circuits developed for implementing the FDDI physical layer functions.

ATM transmission at 155.520 Mbits/s uses 8B/10B coding and the media developed for the **FCS** (Fiber Channel Standard), with blocks of 27 cells, the first of which has special contents and is used as a delineator.

2.3.5   Scrambling cells

Cells are scrambled in order to protect them against false headers, either accidental or intentional. Scrambling also allows the transitions necessary for the correct operation of cell-based transmission systems to be generated. The method consists in adding the sequence of data items, modulo 2, to a pseudo-random sequence produced by a generator polynomial. The type of scrambling depends on the transmission environment:

- In the case of a cell-based transmission system, all the fields in the cell are scrambled. During the cell delineation acquisition phase, pseudo-random sequence synchronization information must be transmitted to the receiver. This information is provided in 2 bits of the HEC field in several cells. During this phase, cell delineation is carried out on only six bits, which explains why a greater number of confirmations are needed (delta = 8) than in synchronous transmission. The polynomial for this type of scrambling is $x^{31} + x^{28} +1$.

- When a synchronous physical layer is used, only the payload is scrambled. Though this system is simpler, it has the disadvantage of doubling transmission errors (to be more precise, the error rate is multiplied by the number of terms of the polynomial used). The polynomial that has been chosen is $x^{43} + 1$.

2.4   Functions of the AAL adaptation layer

2.4.1   Overview

The ATM layer, described above, provides a single, high speed switching service for all the flows generated by applications with very varied profiles. These flows are switched and multiplexed by common mechanisms, and only multiple queues, located before these mechanisms, can provide differentiated handling. The service provided by the ATM layer can be summarized as follows:

- Cell relay operates in connected mode and therefore preserves the sequence order of the cells transmitted.

- The service operates independently of the traffic source's clock. However, this advantage implies that there is no explicit information about the source's clock in the flow received. Furthermore, this asynchronism, added to the presence of queues in the network, introduces variable propagation delays which cause **cell jitter** of about 0.1 ms.

- It does not provide flow control. If necessary, this must be added in the higher layers (user applications).

- It is totally transparent to the cells' payloads. It does not change their contents, but provides no means of checking their integrity. Further, if a transmission error concerning the header is wrongly corrected (when there are multiple errors), there is a risk of imitating a valid logical identifier, and therefore inserting the cell on that logical channel. Conversely, if the HEC correction capacity is exceeded, cells can be lost, which can also happen when the network queues are congested.

The AAL layer is much more strongly linked to the applications: it refines the quality of service provided by the ATM layer according to the requirements of the user service. It implements end-to-end protocols which are transparent to the ATM layer.

In particular, as the information being transferred has no particular reason for being compatible with the length of the ATM cell (48 bytes), the information has to be segmented or grouped on transmission and the cells' contents reassembled or divided on reception.

Different services would therefore require specialized adaptation layers; however, in order to avoid too great a dispersal of efforts, classes of service have been grouped around three main components, which characterize all traffic flows:

- its bit rate, which may be constant or variable;

- its connection mode, which may be connection-oriented or connectionless;

- its requirements from an isochronous point of view, which may impose a strict relationship between the source's clock and that of the receiver, or no relationship whatsoever.

Temporal relationship	with		without	
Bit rate	continuous	variable		
Connection	with			without
	AAL-1	AAL-2	AAL-3/4 or AAL-5	AAL-3/4

Figure 2.12   The types of ATM adaptation

Four types of adaptation derived from combinations of the characteristics mentioned above were first defined: AAL types 1, 2, 3 and 4. Subsequently, AAL types 3 and 4 were combined into one, called AAL type 3/4, and a new AAL **type 5** appeared, due to pressure from the computer world.

This historical reminder illustrates the fact that the list of adaptation mechanisms is not necessarily closed, given their close relationship with users' applications. At present the standardized adaptation mechanisms are (see Figure 2.12):

- AAL type 1, for constant bit rate information which requires a strict relationship between the transmission and reception clocks (for example, voice circuit emulation);

- AAL type 2, for variable bit rate information which also requires a strict relationship between the transmission and reception clocks (for example, variable bit rate video);

- AAL type 3/4, for data transmissions in connection-oriented or connectionless mode;

- AAL type 5, which can be seen as a simplified version of AAL type 3/4 but with similar capabilities.

These adaptation layers are structured into two sublayers:

- The *Segmentation And Reassembly sublayer* (**SAR**) is responsible for changing the format between the user data units and the cell payloads. The AAL fields corresponding to this sublayer, which is relatively independent of the user service, are present in every cell. This function enables lost or duplicated cells to be detected, because they are numbered; nevertheless, recovery itself is the province of the convergence sublayer. Finally, the SAR sub-layer provides for the padding of incomplete cells.

- The *Convergence Sublayer* (**CS**) carries out more specifically user service functions. The AAL fields related to these functions are only present once per user data unit. The convergence sublayer is responsible for error handling if needed: to do so, it implements protocols for retransmitting erroneous data or it protects data, allowing the receiver to correct those errors: this last technique, *Forward Error Correction* (**FEC**), is used in particular for real-time applications. The CS sublayer can also provide end-to-end synchronization.

2.4.2   AAL type 1 adaptation function

The AAL type 1 adaptation function is used by applications with strong isochronous constraints and a constant bit rate, such as:

- voice signals;
- high quality audio signals;
- video signals;
- data circuit emulation.

Its role is to allow the transmitted information's clock pulse to be recovered, to compensate for the differences in propagation time caused by the network and to manage the loss or accidental insertion of cells. It also allows for the use of block-structured data and provides means for handling errors.

The fields related to these functions occupy a byte of the payload, leaving 47 bytes available for the information (see Figure 2.13). They include a *Sequence Number* (**SN**) used to detect missing or accidentally inserted cells, and a *Sequence Number Protection* (**SNP**). The SNP field is divided into two:

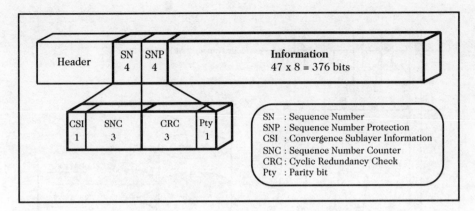

Figure 2.13   AAL type 1

- a 3-bit CRC for correcting single errors;
- a parity bit for detecting double errors.

The SN field is also divided into two:

- The first bit, *Convergence Sublayer Information* (**CSI**), may contain a *Residual Time Stamp* (**RTS**) which is used for setting the receiver's clock. It may also be used to delineate the data blocks;
- The next 3 bits contain the counter for numbering (modulo 8) the cells.

In certain continuous flow applications, such as data circuit emulation or high quality audio signals, it is necessary to reconstitute the information received precisely and therefore to totally absorb cell jitter. In order to do this, the receiver must store the information received for a period of time which is at least equal to the propagation time, plus the maximum value of the jitter (see Figure 2.14).

An asynchronous type transfer, such as ATM, does not allow the source's clock to be controlled by the network clock, so the receiver must restore the source's clock. The cell flow may therefore contain a time stamp (RTS) given by a reference clock. This technique requires the use of a common reference clock derived from the underlying transport network (SDH, for example). This 4-bit time stamp is carried by the CSI bit of one cell in two belonging to a group of eight consecutive cells (odd numbered cells).

In the case of voice or video signals, it is not usually necessary to use the above method, called **SRTS** (*Synchronous Residual Time Stamp*), and the receiver can recover the source's clock approximately from the rhythm at which its memory buffers are filled. The receiver's average incoming filling rate is used to set an initial cell restitution delay. If the filling rate increases, the cell restitution rate accelerates, and conversely if it decreases (see Figure 2.14).

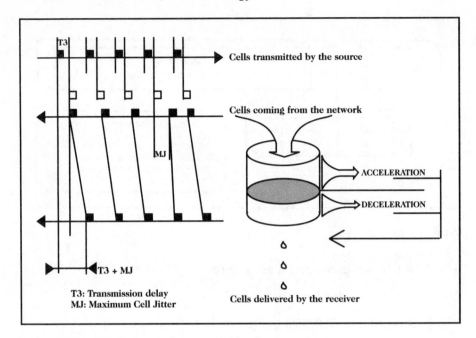

Figure 2.14   Receiver's clock controlled by the transmitter

The AAL type 1 adaptation function also allows block-structured data to be transferred (for example, to support a data circuit at n·64 kbits/s). A pointer, which indicates the location of the next block, makes it possible to delineate the block. This pointer occupies the first byte in the payload (then limited to 46 data bytes) and its presence is indicated by the CSI bit. To ensure compatibility with the SRTS method, described above, the pointer can only be present in even cells.

The AAL type 1 convergence sublayer can also take responsibility for error handling: single or multiple errors in the transmission of the cells' payloads, but also loss or accidental insertion of whole cells, detected by the SAR sublayer. The handling mode and its performance depend on the type of user service: thus, in the case of data circuit emulation, and on condition that the error rate and the cell loss rate are very small, errors can be handled by end-to-end protocols, without AAL layer intervention; similarly, no handling is needed for the telephone service.

Simply detecting a lost cell, with a view to retransmission, is not suitable for real-time applications, because it would involve an unlimited response time. However, it can contribute to the masking of errors by a received information interpolation mechanism. This masking is particularly effective if data has been interleaved on transmission, because this allows the effects of cell loss to be diluted (see the description below).

If error masking is not sufficient to satisfy the user's service constraints (for example, in the case of video signals or high quality audio signals), the original information has to be reconstituted using an FEC type correction technique, which may be combined with an interleaving mechanism.

The principle of *byte interleaving* is based on a very simple idea: if the information is transmitted in cells as and when it is generated, the loss of one cell on reception affects 47 consecutive bytes. On the other hand, the information to be transmitted can be stored temporarily in blocks of 47 times p bytes, after which p cells are made up in the following way: the first contains the bytes numbered 1, $p + 1$, $2p + 1$..., the second the bytes numbered 2, $p + 2$, $2p + 2$... and so on until the cell numbered p is reached. If a cell is lost (the number of that cell is known by the receiver because it detects a sequence break in the SAR sublayer), the reconstituted received flow is only affected by one byte every p bytes, which makes interpolation much easier. We should note that the first cell in p is identified by the CSI bit, which makes this method incompatible with the transfer of block-structured data.

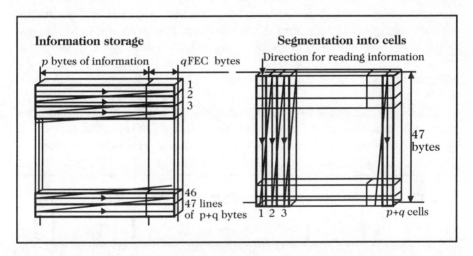

Figure 2.15   The byte interleaving technique

If it is necessary to reconstitute the original set of bytes exactly, a distributed correction technique is added to the interleaving mechanism: instead of storing $47 \cdot p$ bytes directly, q bytes are added to each 'line' of p bytes generated, giving a total of $47 \cdot (p + q)$ bytes. These q bytes are redundant information, calculated from the corresponding p bytes. When the storage memory is read, $p + q$ cells are transmitted, of which q are redundant (see Figure 2.15). In practice, the CCITT recommends the use of a Reed Solomon code RS(128,124), that is $p = 124$ and $q = 4$. If no cells are lost, this code enables up to 2 bytes to be corrected per 'line' of 128 bytes, after reverse interleaving. If the receiver's SAR sublayer detects a lost cell, it provides a dummy cell as a replacement, with an error indication: the correction code can then correct up to four missing cells.

Naturally, such a technique has the disadvantage of introducing a delay of $p + q$ cells, both on transmission and reception; in the above case, a delay equivalent to 256 cells. The lower the bit rate, the greater the problems caused by this delay: in a 384 kbits/s television-telephony application, this mechanism leads to a delay of 250 ms.

Other methods can be imagined. For example, it is possible to transmit a block of p 47-byte cells, without interleaving, followed by a redundant cell, each bit of which indicates the parity of the same bits in the p cells. This technique allows one lost cell to be corrected per block (the cell's number is given by the SAR sublayer).

2.4.3   AAL type 2 adaptation function

The role of this adaptation function is similar to that of the AAL type 1 function, as far as the clock recovery, jitter compensation and cell loss and insertion management functions are concerned. However, the fields corresponding to these functions are different, in order to adapt to the transmission of variable-length data units. They occupy 3 bytes, leaving 45 bytes for the information (see Figure 2.16). There is a 4-bit sequence number, an information type (**IT**) field which describes the type of cell (start or end of message, clock information, and so on), a field indicating the number of significant bytes (**LI**) in the case of a partially filled cell, and a 10-bit CRC code, which enables errors to be detected in the cell's payload and a single error to be corrected.

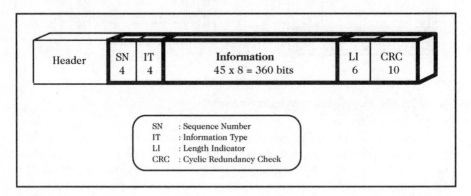

Figure 2.16   AAL type 2

2.4.4   AAL type 3/4 adaptation function

The AAL type 3/4 adaptation function operates either in connection-oriented mode or in connectionless mode, in which the data units (datagrams) are routed independently from each other. The flow carried in connection-oriented mode can be either assured or not by the network:

- In **assured** mode, the AAL type 3/4 layer implements flow control and missing or faulty unit retransmission functions.

- In **non-assured** mode, these functions must be provided by the higher layers.

These adaptation functions accept data units with a maximum length of 65 535 bytes and provide two priority levels: normal priority and high priority.

As Figure 2.17 shows, the convergence sublayer (CS) is made up of two parts called the **CPCS** (*Common Part Convergence Sublayer*) and the **SSCS** (*Service Specific Convergence Sublayer*). The functions related to the assured and non-assured modes of the connection-oriented service are carried out in this latter part.

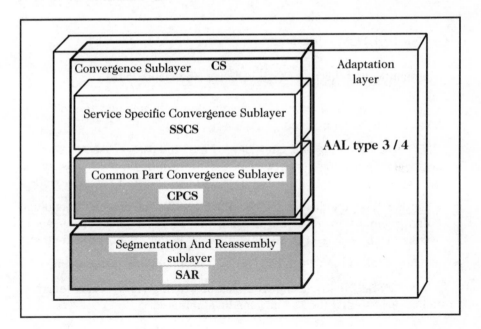

Figure 2.17   AAL type 3/4

The functions provided by the CPCS are the following:

- *Service Data Unit* (CPCS-SDU) delineation;

- error detection (optionally, the faulty CPCS-SDUs can be transmitted to the higher layers with an error indicator, if not they are discarded);

- receiver information about memory needed to receive the CPCS-SDU;

- transmission of an 'abort' message.

The CPCS functions provide support for a connectionless service as well as a connection-oriented service.

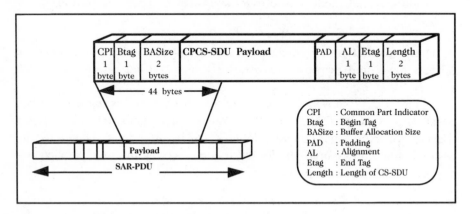

Figure 2.18   CPCS-PDU structure

The significant fields of a CPCS-PDU are (see Figure 2.18) :

- a *Common Part Indicator* (**CPI**) field which indicates how the following fields should be interpreted;

- CPCS-SDU beginning and end (***Btag, Etag***) indicators, used to prevent accidental concatenation of two CPCS-SDU, resulting from the loss of the cells carrying the end of the first data unit and the start of the second;

- a CPCS-SDU size indicator (***BASize***), which tells the receiver how much buffer memory to reserve (so that the receiver does not have to systematically reserve the maximum size of buffer memory, 64 kbytes);

- padding to align the CPCS-SDU on a 32-bit boundary (**AL**, *Alignment*) ;

- a final CPCS-SDU size (***Length***) indicator which gives the exact length of the payload so that the padding can be eliminated.

The SAR sublayer assures the integrity of the cell's payload and provides grouping or ungrouping and segmentation or reassembly functions: units (CS-PDU) smaller than a cell's payload are grouped, whereas larger units are segmented. The fields which provide for these management functions occupy four bytes in the cell, thus reducing the payload to 44 bytes (see Figure 2.19). We should note that this payload size, a multiple of four bytes, is adapted for use by 32-bit processors.

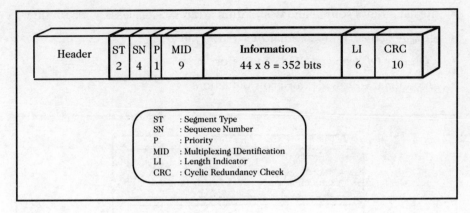

Figure 2.19   SAR-PDU structure

The SAR sublayer fields include:

- a *Segment Type* indicator (**ST**) : start, middle or end of message, or message composed of a single segment;

- a modulo 16 *Sequence Number* (**SN**) for detecting missing or inserted cells;

- a priority indicator, used to transmit high priority SAR-PDU before normal priority ones;

- a *Multiplexing IDentification* (**MID**) indicator, used for identifying cells belonging to different data flows (maximum 512) multiplexed on the same virtual connection;

- a *Length Indicator* (**LI**), which gives the number of bytes (from 1 to 44) used in the cell;

- a 10-bit CRC code, identical to that used in the AAL type 2 adaptation function.

A special coding of a SAR-PDU is used to transmit the abort message: the segment type indicates 'end of message' and the payload is set to zero, as is the LI field.

If a cell relay network is to provide a connectionless service then it must provide additional functions in order to ensure the routing of the datagrams (**CLSF**, *ConnectionLess Service Function*). These functions are defined in a higher layer than AAL type 3/4, which is used in unsecured mode, called **CLNAP** (*ConnectionLess Network Access Protocol*) (see Figure 2.20).

This set of protocols is very similar to that defined in the DQDB standard: addresses based on the E.164 numbering plan, address validation, address groups supported, and so on.

The main fields of the CLNAP layer are the following:

- the datagram's **source** and **destination addresses**, necessary for routing;
- a *Higher Layer Protocol Identifier* (**HLPI**) field;
- a *Quality Of Service* (**QOS**) indicator;
- an optional CRC code, for error detection.

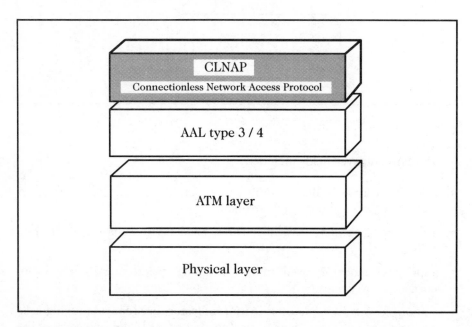

Figure 2.20   Connectionless service

2.4.5   AAL type 5 adaptation function

This function can be seen as a simplified version of layer AAL 3/4: just like that layer, its aim is to transfer data flows made up of variable-length units with a maximum length of 65 535 bytes in connection-oriented mode.

   The data unit sent to AAL type 5 by the user is padded so that it makes a unit which can be divided into an integer number of cells: the length of the resulting unit is then a multiple of 48 bytes, and the length of the padding is between 0 and 47 bytes. The last cell contains 8 bytes dedicated to three different functions:

- a length indicator (16 bits), which the receiver uses to determine the data payload;
- a 32-bit CRC, used to detect errors in the data transferred;
- 16 bits reserved for future use.

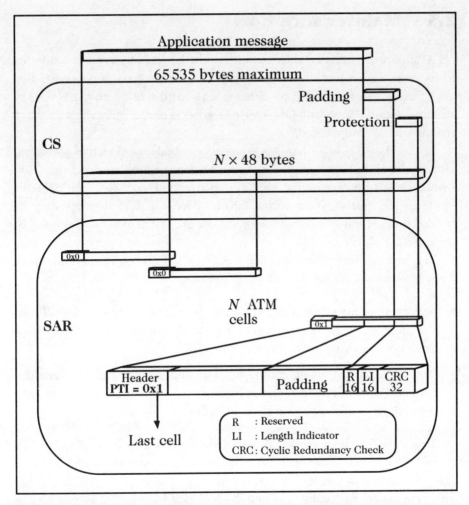

Figure 2.21   AAL type 5 operation

Because all the payload's 48 bytes are occupied by user data, the AAL type 5 function cannot provide any explicit start and end of data unit indicators. The data unit's last cell marker is provided by the last bit of the PTI field (type of SDU = 1) in the ATM header (see page 18). Therefore, the first cell of a data unit is implicitly identified as that which follows the last cell of the previous unit, which is explicitly determined (see Figure 2.21).

The AAL type 5 function is adapted to a hardware implementation of the CPCS sublayer. Its advantage is that it uses the whole of the cells' payloads and implements an effective protection of the data unit using a 32-bit CRC code. However, it does not allow cell-by-cell error detection or the multiplexing of several flows.

2.5   Maintenance flows

An ATM network must be able to measure the quality of service it is offering to its users and detect any degradation. It needs to have ways of locating any faulty components so that it can undertake any necessary reconfiguration. Pinpointing the exact location is particularly valuable when the network is complicated.

Just as the ATM layer handles connections made up of virtual paths and virtual channels, the underlying transmission system is structured into several levels: transmission media, regeneration sections, multiplexing sections, and transmission paths. Furthermore, an ATM network may be divided into several sub-networks (or segments), which may be administered separately.

The maintenance flows are defined in CCITT Recommendation I.610. They are responsible for the following functions:

* performance management, consisting of using a parity check (**BIP**, *Bit Interleaved Parity*) and gathering results (**FEBE**, *Far End Block Error*) to evaluate the error rate;

* fault management, using continuity tests and mechanisms for signalling events (**AIS**, *Alarm Indication Signal*) or returning backwards fault indications (**FERF**, *Far End Receive Failure*).

There are five maintenance flows, as shown in Figure 2.22. Flows F1, F2 and F3 are carried by channels provided by the physical layer, depending on the type of support (framed or continuous flow of cells); flows F4 and F5 use virtual connections (paths or channels) provided by the ATM layer.

2.5.1   Physical layer maintenance flows

Maintenance flows F1, F2 and F3, responsible for monitoring the regeneration section, the multiplexing section (also called the digital section) and the transmission path respectively, mainly use means specific to the transmission system.

In the case of an SDH physical layer, the maintenance flows use the synchronous hierarchy's section (SOH) and path (POH) overheads (see Figure 2.10). Performance measurement is carried out on blocks of bytes whose size is exactly equal to the payload of the virtual containers (2340 bytes for a 155.520 Mbits/s STM-1frame, 9360 bytes for a 622.080 Mbits/s

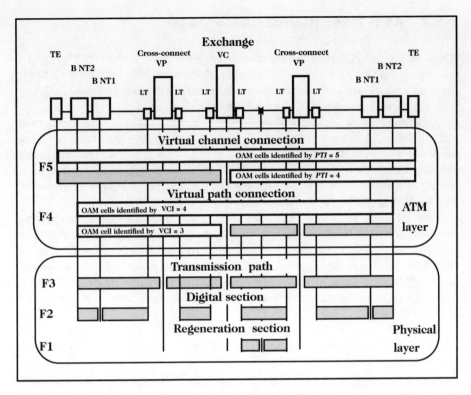

Figure 2.22   ATM maintenance flows

STM-4 frame). Therefore, the parity check is applied to all the bytes in the cells (headers included) transported by the containers. In the case of flows F1 and F3, it is carried out byte by byte (BIP-8), whereas in the case of flow F2, it is applied to 3-byte words (BIP-24) at 155.520 Mbits/s or 6-byte words (BIP-96) at 622.080 Mbits/s.

Similarly, the PDH physical layer uses certain binary elements of the 34.368 and 139.264 Mbits/s systems' overheads for the maintenance flows. The parity check (BIP-8) is again applied to the whole of the payload, that is 530 or 2160 bytes.

The physical layer of a cell-based system does not provide *a priori* any specific means of communication for the maintenance flows. In this case, special maintenance cells (**OAM**, *Operation, Administration and Maintenance*) are regularly inserted in the cell flow. They are identified by a specific header, which also indicates whether it is an F1 type flow or an F3 type flow (note that a cell-based system does not have a multiplexing section). Performance measurement is carried out on a fixed number of cells. The OAM cells may contain parity check information (BIP-8), results (number of parity errors) or AIS and FERF indications. Their contents are protected by a 10-bit CRC (polynomial $x^{10} + x^9 + x^5 + x^4 + x + 1$).

2.5.2   ATM layer maintenance flows

Whereas the physical layer flows can only be accessed by the network operator, the F4 and F5 maintenance flows can be used by the user. Generally, they are only activated on request. They are end-to-end flows, but there are also segment flows (sub-network flows).

A virtual path is checked (flow F4) by sending OAM cells on a reserved virtual channel (VCI = 4 for an end-to-end F4 flow, VCI = 3 for a sub-network F4 flow). Maintenance flows involving a given virtual channel (flow F5) take the same path as the operational cells: they are distinguished by a special coding of the PTI field in their headers (PTI = 5 if the F5 flow is end to end, PTI = 4 if it applies to a sub-network).

The F4 and F5 flows call use the same mechanism for measuring performance. It is implemented on nominal sized blocks (N = 128, 256, 512 or 1024 cells). The OAM parity check (BIP-16) cell is only inserted after N cells when there is no activity, so as not to cause jitter in the operational flow. Insertion is forced if there has been no activity for 3N/2 cells; the next insertion remains fixed at 2N and the protected block then has a reduced size of N/2 cells.

In order to check that a connection is still active, test cells can be sent when no working cell has been transmitted during a given period and no fault has been signalled.

2.6   Cell relay performance

The parameters that affect cell relay performance are:

- loss of cells;
- transfer delay.

2.6.1   Loss of cells

There are two major causes of cell loss: header errors and buffer overflows. Even though the header is protected against errors, some are neither corrected nor detected, which leads to routing errors. Furthermore, error handling by the HEC leads to cells whose headers contain uncorrectable errors being discarded. Cell relay is therefore subject to a cell loss rate and an incorrect routing rate.

The sizes of the buffer are not infinite, and there is a probability of cell loss due to overflow. This loss depends on the number of flows multiplexed on the same route, on the sizes of the buffer located on that route and on the nature of the flows multiplexed. The buffer sizes and the number of flows multiplexed are determined according to the acceptable cell loss target. Figure 2.23 shows targets for different information flows.

The numbers indicated in this figure are widely divergent . These values must be maintained in order to guarantee a good quality of service for each flow. One way of guaranteeing a good quality of service for each information flow is to provide a large number of service classes. However, any increase in the number of service classes also increases the complexity of the network.

	Format	Target
Telephone quality voice	CCITT G.711 PCM (64 kbits/s)	$< 10^{-3}$
High quality voice	CCITT G.727 SB-ADPCM (64 kbits/s)	$< 10^{-5}$
Standard quality television	Signal compression (10 Mbits/s on average)	$< 10^{-9}$
High definition television	Signal compression (100 Mbits/s on average)	$< 10^{-10}$
Data transmission	HDLC (64 kbits/s to 100 Mbits/s)	$< 10^{-6}$

Figure 2.23   Cell loss rate targets

The use of the cell loss priority bit helps in achieving a cell loss target, for a given class of service, by indicating cells carrying less important information which can be discarded (see page 21). This technique is feasible for video flows, but it is more difficult to implement for data transmissions, where all the bits are *a priori* equally important.

2.6.2   Transfer delay

For a given information flow, the global delay affecting the cells depends on three main factors:

T1   the coding and decoding time;

T2   the time required for segmentation and reassembly;

T3   the time taken to transfer cells across the network.

Information coding and decoding

T1 depends on the type of coding used: a G.711 type coding (PCM at 64 kbits/s) only adds a few milliseconds, whereas a more sophisticated technique produces less information for transmission but takes more coding and decoding time (several tens of milliseconds).

Segmentation and reassembly

T2, the time required for segmentation and reassembly, can be broken down into two factors: the transmitter segmentation delay (**T21**) and the delay (**T22**) introduced in the receiver to compensate for the variations in cell transfer time.

Segmentation of M bytes of information into cells causes a delay T21 which depends on the bit rate D (expressed in bits per second), and can be approximately evaluated by **8M/D**. This delay decreases as the bit rate increases.

Cells inserted at a regular rhythm by an information source are not delivered regularly by the network (see page 35). Asynchronous transfer mode introduces variations in the transfer delay. The receiver must compensate for them, and therefore add a delivery delay which will allow it to absorb the largest differences.

Transfer across the network

T3, the time taken to transfer cells across the network, is the sum of the propagation delay of the transmission media (T31) and the transit time (T32) spent in the switching nodes.

T31, the propagation delay, is a function of the distance and the number and nature of the physical media used between the source and the destination. Transmission on fibre optics introduces a delay of about 5 ms per 1000 km. The longest terrestrial distance produces a delay not longer than 50 ms, compared to 300 ms for a satellite link.

T32 includes the time the cells have to wait in the buffer and the time taken to insert them into the physical transmission supports. This time is a direct function of the bit rate used (about 3 μs per cell at 155.520 Mbits/s). The time the cells have to wait in the buffer depends on the dimensioning of the nodes: an average filling level of 100 cells causes an average delay of 300 μs per node (100 × 3 μs). The global delay then depends on the number of nodes the cell passes through.

Global delay target

The information flow that generates the most restrictive delay target is voice: let **T0** be that target's value. Two of the delay components described above are variable and influence the dimensioning of the network (the number and the capacity of links and switching nodes):

T22   the transfer delay variation compensation time;

T32   the time spent waiting in the switching nodes' buffers.

The other components (T1, T21 and T31) are more or less fixed and known for any given environment. T22 and T32 must therefore be selected so that the following is true:

$$T22 + T32 < T0 - T1 - T21 - T31$$

ATM switching units

3.1 Introduction

A complex network is made up of interconnected switching units. The role of a switching unit is to set up a connection between an input port and an output port, according to the routing information. Before describing the specific constraints of ATM, we will summarize the principles and limitations of conventional switching modes.

3.1.1 Circuit switching

The technique known as 'space division switching' consists in physically linking an input port of the switching unit to one of its output ports for the duration of a communication (for example, a telephone call). This technique introduces a constant and very short delay, because the switching unit does not store the information.

Time division synchronous switching uses time slots which are assigned to the channels being switched. It operates with physical supports which are time division multiplexed according to a fixed-length frame structure. The

51

information corresponding to an input multiplexer's time slot is stored temporarily and then delivered at regular intervals, in an equivalent frame but in a different time slot, to one or more output multiplexers chosen by the switching unit. The correspondence between the time slots of the multiplexers, which switch between input and output channels, is independent of the use made of the channels and the bit rates do not depend on the sources of information, but solely on the characteristics of the multiplexing system being used (bit rate, frame structure).

3.1.2 Packet switching

This is a case of asynchronous time division switching: the packets, made up of data blocks accompanied by a pointer contained in the header, are received on the switching unit's input links at a speed that depends solely on the source. Each packet is stored and then delivered to the output link determined by the routing information contained in a table. The entry accessed in the table depends on the pointer's value. The storage time, and therefore the time the packet is delayed, is variable because of the statistical sharing of resources.

A feature of a datagram service is the fact that the packets are independently switched according to their explicit destination addresses, and that no previous marking is necessary. By contrast, in the case of a 'logical channel' type service, where the sequence of packets must be maintained, the technique used consists in making the packets for a given connection follow the same path, identified by a series of pointers. In practice, in a complex network, there may be several possible paths between a given input point and a given output point.

The switching function is usually carried out by software. Other functions, such as flow control and retransmission on error, may be undertaken by the same processor or may be left to the accesses. Normal performance is several thousand packets switched per second, with a composite global speed of several Mbits/s; the delay is in the order of 10 or 100 ms.

The required characteristics of an ATM switching unit are completely different:

- very high access speeds mean there will be a global bit rate of several Gbits/s;
- several million cells are switched per second;
- there must be a stable and very small delay (less than 1 ms), to provide circuit emulation;
- there must be a low cell loss rate.

This is only possible using a hardware **switch fabric** which is highly parallel. This switch fabric may be made up of several identical **switching components**, which may be organized into a multi-level structure.

3.2   ATM switching unit functions

As well as **analysing** and **modifying the header** (new VPI/VCI values), an ATM switching unit provides two main functions, described below (see Figure 3.1):

- **routing** cells to the appropriate output ports;

- temporarily **storing** cells.

The switching unit must also manage several parallel cell flows differentiated by **priority** levels and provide preferential handling for high priority cells (for example, by implementing queues for each priority level).

Finally, certain ATM services require the **broadcasting** of cells coming from the same source: broadcast, to all destinations, or *multicast*, to a predetermined set of destination accesses. Of course, the source itself could provide distinct copies of each of the cells to be broadcast, but these copies would be routed as so many independent flows, which would lead to a waste of bandwidth and would mean that the source would have to know the complete list of destination addresses.

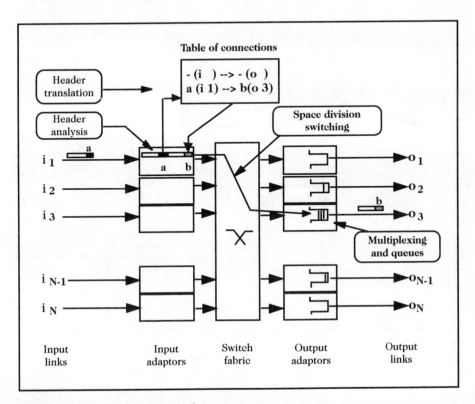

Figure 3.1   ATM switching unit functions

A more efficient method is to shift the point where the cells are duplicated as far forward as possible: using a particular item of information (broadcast address), an ATM switching unit should be able to replicate the same cell to several output ports.

As shown diagramatically in Figure 3.1, the header is usually handled by the switching unit's input adaptors, which are responsible for recovering the flow of valid cells from the input links. The routing is carried out by the switching fabric. The temporary storage of cells usually takes place in the output and/or input adaptors, but may also be centralized in the switching fabric.

3.2.1   Routing cells

Generally, the connection between an input port and an output port, which determines the route through the switching fabric, must be previously known and stored in the table of connections. This information may be held as a marker which establishes a specific path for transferring the cells related to a given connection (**indirect routing**), or as a label which, when added to the cells to be transferred, allows them to direct themselves to the appropriate output port (**self-routing**).

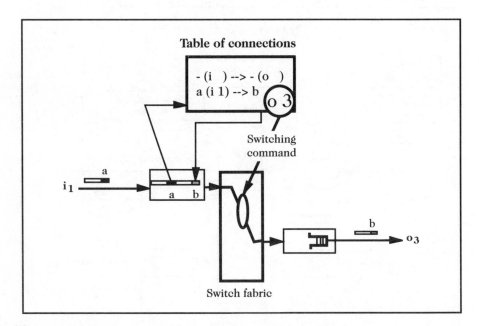

Figure 3.2   Indirect routing in an ATM switching unit

As the ATM service is connection-oriented, the natural routing mode is indirect: each cell's header contains a pointer (VPI/VCI) whose value identifies the connection, and which only has a local meaning (see page 19). The path corresponding to that connection must be explicitly written to every switching component before any information is transferred. Cells are then routed to the appropriate output port by consulting the table: for each VPI/VCI value there is a corresponding output port and a new pointer value (see Figure 3.2). Potentially, the table can be very large, because each connection is identified by 24 or 28 bits in the cell's header.

One way of implementing this routing, at the cost of an overhead, consists in using self-routing: at the input to each switching unit (especially if it is made up of several switching components), an additional routing label is added to each cell. It describes the physical route the cells must take and is in the form of a list of identifiers of the switching components they must traverse and the output ports they must use (see Figure 3.3).

All the cells related to a given connection follow the same route and are delivered to the receiver in sequence. The switching components do not mark them, because the route is written explicitly in each label. The information which has been used is removed from the label's contents (sometimes called a 'consumable label') as the cell makes its way through the switching unit (instead of deleting part of the label, a pointer which indicates the remaining useful part can be modified).

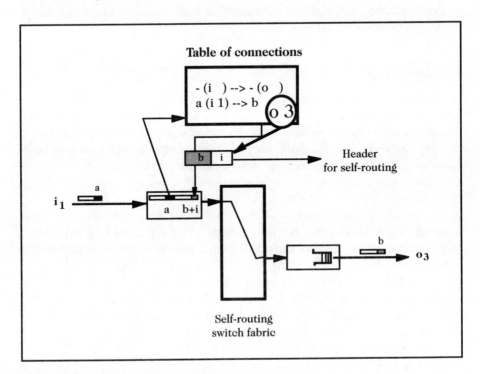

Figure 3.3   Self-routing in an ATM switching unit

3.2.2   Temporary storage of cells

In certain switch fabrics there is a risk of internal blocking because it is not always possible to establish a path between an input port and an available output port (in particular, this is the case for Banyan type switching units described on page 60). It is therefore natural to think that in order to avoid unacceptable loss rates, storage devices (queues) are essential at the inputs or inside the switching unit.

However, even if a non-blocking switch fabric is used, cells still have to be stored temporarily in order to resolve **output contention**. In practice, due to the statistical nature of the incoming traffic, several cells received on different input ports can be in competition for simultaneous access to the same output port.

There are two classic approaches to the location of queues: *input queuing* or *output queuing* in the switch. There are others, but for the most part they can be seen as variants or combinations of these two. The following paragraphs describe these methods, using the following hypotheses:

- the switching unit involved is of the $N \times N$ type (N input ports and N output ports operating at the same speed);

- the input traffic flows are independent and statistically identical; they are uniform, and each cell has a probability equal to $1/N$ of having a given output point as its destination.

Input queuing

A **FIFO** (*First In First Out*) queue is associated with each input port. A contention is detected if j cells ($j \leq N$) located at the head of j queues are destined for the same output. This approach is natural enough in that it detects the contention before the switching fabric is reached and only supplies cells that can reach their destination (see Figure 3.4). However, all the cells further back in the $j - 1$ queues which are not serviced are also blocked, even if they are destined for ports which are free at the time.

This *Head Of Line blocking* (**HOL**) effect limits the performance of input queuing. It can be shown that, if N is large, the load offered by the switch fabric cannot exceed a value equal to $2 - \sqrt{2}$, that is, about 0.58, whatever the queue arbitration algorithm (random, cyclical...), if it is equitable (note that for $N = 4$, the maximum load is already limited to 0.65).

The input queuing method is poorly adapted to broadcast functions, because there are no output queues. Furthermore, it is very susceptible to non-uniform input traffic. On the other hand, it has the advantage of being very simple and does not require a switch fabric operating speed higher than the access speed.

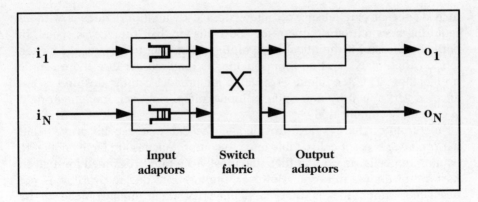

Figure 3.4   Input queuing of cells

Better performance can be achieved at the cost of greater complexity, for example by increasing the internal speed of the switch fabric. Another improvement consists in sorting the cells on entry according to their destination, which means managing N queues per input port (one for each output port).

Output queuing

In this approach, a FIFO queue is associated with each output port (see Figure 3.5). All the cells presented to the input ports at any given time traverse the switch fabric at the same time and are then stored. As they may all have the same destination, the queue associated with the output port involved must be capable of storing N cells.

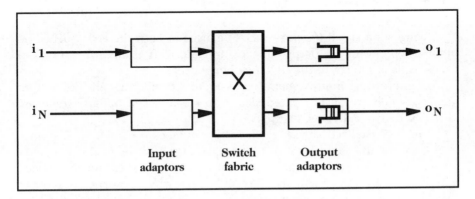

Figure 3.5   Output queuing (unlimited size queues)

Fast conventional type queues can be used if the internal speed of the switch fabric is N times greater than the speed of the ports. Conversely, a high degree of parallelism will allow storage in multiport queues without requiring a switch fabric operating speed higher than the access speed. In both these cases, if the queues are of unlimited size, the use of the switch fabric is optimized, and no input queuing is required because there can be no blocking. This technique is suitable for broadcast functions and is not affected very much by non-uniform input traffic. However, implementing it is extremely complicated.

In terms of the bit rate provided or the delay, it can be proved that performance is practically stable once the output queues are large enough to contain ten cells, as we find that statistically the bursts destined for a given port are of limited duration. However, the loss rate due to overflow is not negligible, which means that supplementary input queues need to be installed (see Figure 3.6); the size of these queues depends on the real characteristics of the traffic and the admissible loss rate.

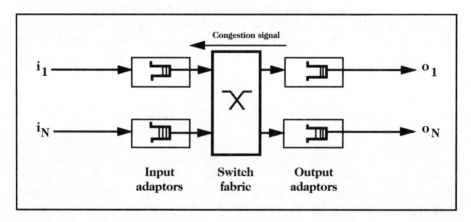

Figure 3.6   Output queuing (limited size queues)

A congestion signal (*back pressure*) is used to keep the cells queued on input when the target output queues are full. This backwards storing of excess cells is subject to the *HOL blocking* effect.

An interesting improvement consists in considering all the output queues, which are all of limited size, as a single set of buffers which are allocated dynamically (see Figure 3.7).

Using a centralized storage such as this reduces the amount of storage necessary for the same level of performance by a factor of three or four, compared with the technique of dedicated output queues. An overloaded output port can temporarily use several buffers, which statistically reduces the use of the supplementary input buffers. This statistical multiplexing effect becomes more marked as the number of ports, N, increases.

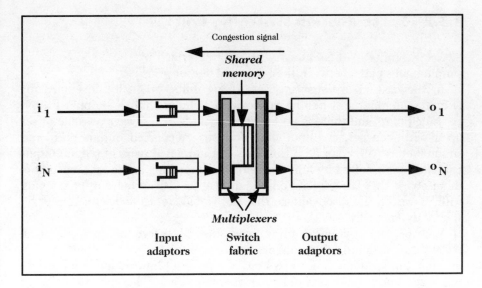

Figure 3.7   Centralized cell queuing

3.3   Types of switching fabric

ATM switching units can be grouped into two categories, according to their architectures: shared resource switching units and space division switching units.

3.3.1   Shared resource switching units

These work on the principle of multiplexing all the input flows towards a very high capacity shared resource.

Some switching units, organized around a **shared memory**, benefit from the advantages of the centralized storage described above. The management of this centralized memory is complicated and its bandwidth is very broad, which means a high degree of parallelism has to be implemented in order to overcome technological constraints.

Others use a **shared medium** to connect the input ports to the queues associated with the output ports. This medium is usually a bus or a ring which transfers several bits in parallel.

3.3.2   Space division switching units

Switching units in this category are characterized by the coexistence of simultaneous paths between the input and output ports.

In the case of **crossbar** type switching units, originally developed for circuit switching, a switching fabric with N inputs and N outputs has N^2 crossing points and there is no internal blocking: it is always possible to set up a path between an input port and an unoccupied output port, and simultaneous paths can be set up between unrelated pairs of ports. Output contention is resolved by input queuing or by queuing in the crossing points themselves: this latter technique is similar to distributed output queuing with, however, the disadvantage that the global storage capacity cannot be shared dynamically.

Banyan type switching units have the advantage of only requiring $(N/2) \cdot \log_2 N$ switching components to form a matrix of N inputs and N outputs. For example, an 8×8 matrix requires 12 switching components organized into three stages of four components each. These are of the 2×2 type, which can connect each input to one of two outputs, depending on a cell destination address bit (self-routing). However, switch fabrics of this type can become blocked internally: there is only one path between a given input and a given output and there may be contentions for the use of an internal link.

Conventional input queuing and queuing inside the switching components are possible, but it can also be demonstrated that a Banyan network will not block if its inputs are ordered in relation to its outputs, in so far as there is no more than one cell per output port. This sort function can be carried out by a supplementary switching network (**Batcher** network) located in front of the Banyan network. One technique for the resolution of output contention, when several cells are destined for the same port, consists in only letting one of them through and sending the others back to the input to be sorted again.

4

Broadband ISDN

4.1 Overview

The aim of the broadband integrated services digital network (ISDN) is to carry all types of information (voice, sound, video, text, images and data) on a single network. Installing a limited number of interfaces is one of the essential aims of this multi-service network. In this context, ATM technology is particularly suitable for the multiplexing and switching functions. The services should be available on virtual connections which are set up permanently or on request, that is, call by call. Services in connectionless mode are also planned.

Fibre optics seem to be the indispensable medium, as far as transmission functions are concerned, capable of providing the capacity and performance necessary for high speed services. Synchronous digital transmission, mentioned on page 29, is the natural partner for the installation of broadband ISDN: the SDH system will be used as the network's physical layer, whereas ATM will optimize the use of these supports and be the basis for the services offered.

The worldwide installation of such a network can only happen progressively. Therefore, the way in which it interoperates with existing networks will be a prime factor in the success of broadband ISDN.

4.2 The architecture of broadband ISDN

The architecture of broadband ISDN is based on the concept of separate planes, which ensure the segregation of three groups of functions: user, control and management (see Figure 4.1).

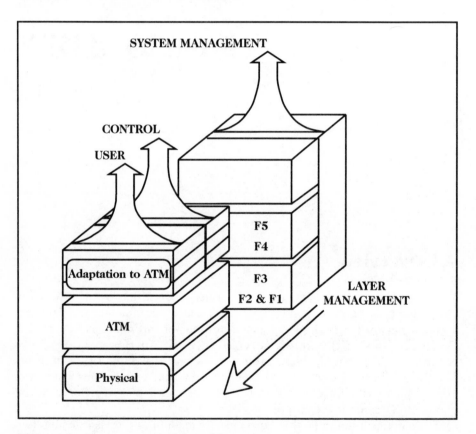

Figure 4.1   Separation into planes of functions

As well as being segregated into planes according to the stacks of protocols used, broadband ISDN is also based on a segmentation of the network which is largely based on its predecessor, narrowband ISDN (see Figure 4.2), where two sub-networks support the services:

- the distribution network between the subscriber and the local access switching unit, which may use a continuous flow of cells or synchronous digital frames;

- the backbone network, which connects the local access switching units using synchronous digital transmission.

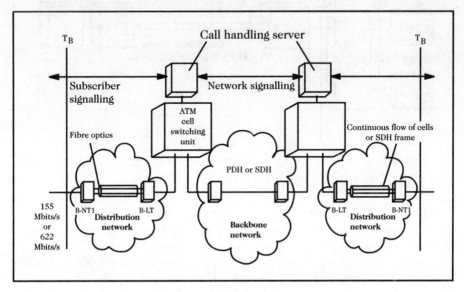

Figure 4.2   Broadband ISDN architecture

The segregation of the protocol stacks into planes and the segmentation of the network into sub-networks gives two reference models, which we will describe below.

4.2.1 The configuration reference model

The use of a reference model is extremely useful when it comes to describing a complex environment. This model, which was inherited from narrowband ISDN, is made up of functional groups with points of reference between them, which may or may not be realized as physical interfaces.

Three main functional groups have been defined at the frontier between the distribution network and the domain of the user who is a subscriber to broadband ISDN services. Two of them are located one on each side of the access link:

- switching unit side, the *Broadband Line Termination* (**B-LT**), which connects the broadband switching unit to the optical link;

- subscriber side, the *Broadband Network Termination 1* (**B-NT1**), which connects the **subscriber installation** and is the last element in the distribution network.

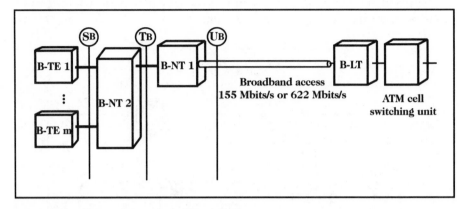

Figure 4.3   Connection to broadband ISDN

The B-NT1 line terminating equipment connects the installation to the network using an interface at reference point T_B. The subscriber installation is made up of a group of terminals (**B-TE**, *Broadband Terminal Equipment*) connected either directly to the network or via switching units (**B-NT2**, *Broadband Network Termination 2* or digital subscriber termination). Figure 4.3 shows the reference configuration for a broadband connection.

The digital subscriber termination (B-NT2) is the framework of the subscriber installation and covers a large number of functions:

- managing the interfaces at reference points S_B and T_B;

- managing shared supports, such as the local area networks;

- managing the signalling between the subscriber and the access switching unit;

- determining the traffic's profile and allocating resources;

- switching and multiplexing ATM cells;

- adapting the information flows to the ATM cell format;

- supporting internal communications and filtering the incoming and outgoing communications of the subscriber installation.

A broadband **PBX** (*Private Branch eXchange*), a data flow multiplexer and a communications controller are examples of the sort of equipment that can accommodate this kind of functional group (B-NT2).

A *Broadband Terminal Adaptor* (**B-TA**) is used to connect terminals, which are not compatible with the interface at reference point S_B.

4.2.2 The protocols reference model

We will understand the division of functions in the environment based on ATM better if we look at the protocols reference model. Figure 4.1 on page 62 shows the relationship between the planes and the layers. This model has three planes:

- the user plane, responsible for the information flow generated, with error detection and recovery when necessary;

- the control plane, which manages the calls and the connections they entail: it includes support for the signalling system used for connecting the subscriber (see page 68);

- the management plane, which contributes to the management of the various protocol stacks (*Layer Management*) and to system administration (*System Management*).

This architecture is based on three shared layers:

- the physical layer, which directly depends on the transmission system;

- the ATM layer, which uses the physical layer's services and provides cell switching, multiplexing and routing functions;

- the adaptation layer, which provides a service to the flows coming from the control plane or the user plane.

The adaptation layer resides in a terminal (B-TE) or in a digital subscriber termination (B-NT2). It is also found in the network switching units for interoperating services, where it provides the interface with the control plane.

4.2.3 Reference points

Reference point T_B is the frontier, at least in Europe, between the operator domain and the user domain. Reference point U_B should play this role in the context of the current liberalization which is opening up all subscriber equipment to competition, but because it has not been defined, point U_B will not be discussed in this chapter. Beyond point T_B, the subscriber installation usually requires a distribution structure in order to reach the terminals. The following two notions will be discussed separately:

- the interface at reference point T_B;

- the subscriber's distribution structure in the context of broadband ISDN.

The interface at reference point T_B

Broadband ISDN uses a new generation of user–network connections, based in principle on the use of fibre optics in the distribution network. The characteristics of the interface at reference point T_B are as follows:

- the interface may be electrical (coaxial cable) or optical (mono-mode fibre);

- the real bit rate is 155.520 or 622.080 kbits/s;

- the interface's structure is made up of a continuous flow of ATM cells or G.709 synchronous frames;

- the signals are coded in **CMI** (*Coded Mark Inversion*) for an electrical interface, or in **NRZ** (*Non Return to Zero*) for an optical interface.

This set of variants means there are several interfaces at reference point T_B, given the possible choices between interface structures (synchronous frames or continuous flow of cells) and transmission technologies (electrical or optical).

Distribution structure

There are two modes for connecting several terminals to a broadband digital access:

- connecting each terminal (B-TE) to a single device that provides the switching functions;

- using a connection based on the distribution of the switching functions to the terminals, which are themselves distributed along a bus or ring.

These two connection modes give, in turn, three types of topologies for the subscriber distribution structure: star, bus or ring, as shown in Figure 4.4.

A shared transmission channel is used for the bus and ring configurations. The first four bits of the ATM cell's header are used at the user network interface (UNI) by the protocol which is responsible for equitable sharing of the transmission medium, thus allowing transfer of the traffic from each of the active terminals. These bits are called the **GFC** (*Generic Flow Control*). There are two operational modes:

- **uncontrolled mode**, in which the GFC bits are ignored on reception and set to zero on transmission, is used for point-to-point configuration;

- **controlled mode**, in which two groups of protocols are under consideration: DQDB type protocols and cyclic type protocols. At present no consensus has been reached on standardization and several proposals are still being studied. This mode is used for **point-to-multipoint configuration**.

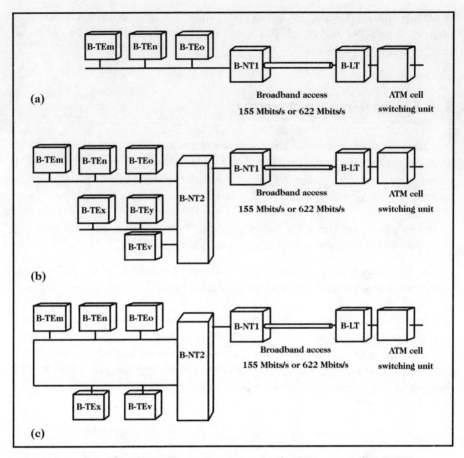

Figure 4.4   Subscriber distribution structure. (a) Bus; (b) star with B-NT2; (c) ring with B-NT2.

These various structures coexist, because the choice between them is always the result of a technical-economic compromise depending, amongst other things, on:

- the number and type of terminals;
- the nature of the site (campus, tower block, isolated premises, for example);
- equipment management;
- the technological characteristics.

Whether the switching function is centralized or distributed, it always provides an interface at reference point S_B which is independent of the distribution structure (see Figure 4.4). The definition of this interface is still the subject of standardization work. The debate is still open between identical characteristics to reference point T_B (the option chosen for narrowband ISDN) and much lower speeds, better adapted to the needs of the terminals.

4.3 Signalling systems

Very flexible management of the bit rate assigned to each virtual connection is one of the main characteristics of the ATM technique. In particular, ATM allows a call set-up procedure which optimizes the use of the network's resources. This procedure can be divided into two phases:

- the establishment of a virtual connection between the terminal and the network, without allocation of the necessary resources;

- the allocation of resources, but only if the called terminal is both available and compatible with the calling terminal.

The allocation of resources is under the control of two signalling systems which cover the syntax and the semantics of the information exchanged between the user and the network or between nodes in the network. This information, which for a long time was limited to rudimentary signals, has now taken the form of structured messages on digital networks, especially on narrowband ISDN.

4.3.1 Signalling at the user–network interface

The signalling system used between the user connection and the local exchange is an extended variant of the protocol used by narrowband ISDN, **DSS-1** (*Digital Signalling System-1*). DSS-1 contains two levels of protocol: Q.921 and Q.931. The data link protocol, Q.921, which transports the Q.931 format signalling messages, is not good enough for high speed connections and has been replaced by a protocol which is better adapted to that environment. This new protocol, called **SSCOP** (*Service Specific Connection Oriented Protocol or Q.21X0*), uses a new adaptation layer called **SAAL** (Signalling ATM Adaptation Layer), whose main characteristics are derived from AAL type 5.

SSCOP completes the service provided by the underlying adaptation mechanism: because this layer does not implement error handling, the service provided by AAL type 5 is a non-assured transfer of data units. At high speeds, even a short delay makes the classic 'go back on error' procedure (*go back-N*), used in HDLC type protocols, inefficient: the number

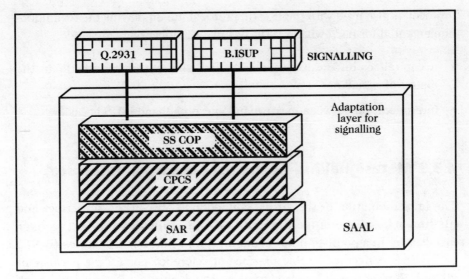

Figure 4.5   Relationship between the signalling systems and the adaptation layer

of data units that have to be retransmitted increases because the amount of data transmitted but not acknowledged is equal to the bit rate multiplied by the medium's transmission delay.

Therefore, SSCOP proposes an error recovery procedure which only retransmits the faulty units, at the most convenient time. This procedure is a variation of an HDLC mode, *Balanced Check Mode*, developed for satellite links on which the large delay makes the *go back-N* mode inefficient for relatively low bit rates.

A extended Q.931 protocol (Q.2931) has been developed to take the characteristics of broadband services into account: a separate virtual connection is used for the signalling between the subscriber access and the local exchange. Figure 4.5 shows the relationship between the signalling and adaptation layers.

4.3.2 Signalling at the network-to-network interface

With the advent of narrowband ISDN, a specific system for signalling between network nodes became generalized: signalling system no.7 (SS-7). This internal network signalling system has also been modified to take into account the characteristics of broadband services. The **ISUP** protocol (*Integrated Service User Part* or Q.761/4), equivalent to Q.931 for SS-7, has been extended to become **B-ISUP** (Q.2761/4).

The SSCOP protocol, which is already used to protect the integrity of the data transferred between the subscriber and the network, using the Q.2931 protocol, is also used with the B-ISUP protocol. Re-employing the techniques implemented for narrowband ISDN has two significant advantages:

- it capitalizes on the experience gained with narrowband ISDN in the matter of signalling;

- interoperation between narrowband and broadband ISDN is easier.

4.3.3 Metasignalling at the user–network interface

The implementation of the virtual connection between the subscriber and his/her access exchange depends on the configuration of the user installation. In a **point-to-point configuration**, where a single device (B-NT2 or B-TE) is connected to the interface at reference point T_B, a permanent virtual connection is used: virtual channel number 5 on virtual path number 0.

On the other hand, if the configuration allows several devices to share the digital access (**point-to-multipoint configuration**), a **metasignalling** procedure is required to manage the configuration. The exchange occurs on a meta-channel which is virtual channel number 1 (on virtual path number 0). Furthermore, a *Broadcast Signalling Virtual Channel* (**BSVC**) is used to present an incoming call to all the devices in the 'multipoint' configuration so that they can determine their level of compatibility with the calling device. This broadcast channel is identified by virtual channel number 2 on virtual path number 0. Therefore, there is one meta-channel and one broadcast channel per interface. This number can be increased by changing the virtual path number.

The metasignalling procedure, which the CCITT is in the process of standardizing (Q.142X), is similar to that of assigning an identifier to a terminal (**TEI**, *Terminal End-point Identifier*) on the narrowband ISDN passive bus. As in the case of narrowband ISDN, it is managed by the management plane and not the control plane. Its main functions are the following:

- setting up, releasing and checking the status of virtual signalling channels;

- resolving contentions in the allocation of virtual signalling channel and path identifiers;

- managing the bit rate assigned to the virtual signalling channels.

4.4 Services offered by broadband ISDN

Once again, we go back to the principles of ISDN: bearer services, teleservices and supplementary services. The bearer services are based on the asynchronous transfer mode which handles any type of information flow as a continuous succession of ATM cells, and are complemented by the appropriate adaptation functions. This architecture means that the following bearer services can be offered on the broadband interface:

- a virtual circuit service, permanent or on request, where the bandwidth is reserved (circuit emulation);

- a virtual circuit service, permanent or on request, where the bandwidth is allocated statistically (equivalent to packet switching);

- a datagram service based on E.164 addressing.

In general, these services already exist, but only on specific networks with limited speeds. When they become available on a single interface it should make multimedia communication easier. However, given the amount of investment necessary, the introduction of broadband ISDN will be gradual. Any operator introducing a service will have to reconcile two contradictory objectives:

- a service can only be developed if it is based on a network with a large geographic coverage;

- the initial investment cannot exceed the real demand if it is not to compromise the development's financial viability.

Therefore, the broadband ISDN start-up phase can only be based on services for which the demand is both limited, in terms of the population, and restricted, from a geographical point of view.

4.5   ATM pilot projects

A Memorandum of Understanding (MoU) was signed between European Public Network Operators (PNOs) in two stages:

- BT, Deutsche Bundespost Telekom, France Telecom, Telefonica (Spain), IRITEL and Società Finanziaria Telefonica (STET, Italy).

- Belgacom, Norwegian Telecom, PTT Telecom Netherlands, Telecom Finland, Telephones de Lisboa-Porto (TLP, Portugal), Televerket (Sweden) and Swiss PTT, who line up with the initial group.

A European Virtual Path (VP) infrastructure based on ATM VP cross-connects has been up and running for 12 months. Under the MoU, each PNO has installed at least one ATM node conforming to ETSI standards. The nodes were interconnected initially by 34.386 Mbits/s links and later by 139.264 or 155.520 Mbits/s links.

Several high speed services presently offered on dedicated platforms are being trialled on that platform, such as frame relay, CBDS and Constant Bit Rate (CBR) services. The provision of higher layer switching capabilities for these services and the procurement of equipment remain the responsibility of each national operator. The trial is aimed at testing the interconnection of existing and/or planned national broadband trials and/or services (for example, SuperJanet, see below). The broadband infrastructure includes both ATM islands and MANs based on DQDB.

Another goal of the trial is to validate standards from ETSI and specifications from Eurescom. In particular, the trial is being used to test the new ETSI standard for ATM cell mapping over PDH rates (for example, 34.386 Mbits/s). That method, where cells are self-delineated, has been preferred to the less efficient PLCP enveloping derived from SMDS.

Eurescom is a research institute created by the 26 PNOs belonging to CEPT to support PNOs in the development of pan-European services. Eurescom currently assists the PNOs in developing three technologies: ATM, TMN (Telecomunication Management Network) and IN (Intelligent Network). Eurescom is based in Heidelberg and produces functional specifications for field trials and recommendations for post-trial strategies.

The pilot network interconnects the research centres of the PNOs that have signed the MoU and pilot users attached to the national broadband trials. A number of broadband trials and services are given below with reference to their planned or anticipated connection to the MoU trial: the trials from BT, Deutsche Bundespost Telekom and France Telecom are described, and then the situation in the other European countries is summarized, as well as in the United States.

4.5.1   BT

In the UK, SuperJanet (Joint Academic NETwork) provides the academic community with a high performance network. It complements the X.25 service, available at several academic locations, currently served by the existing Janet network. It comprises two independent elements:

- a high speed transmission system linking a dozen sites at 139.264 Mbits/s (PDH), shortly to be upgraded to 155.520 Mbits/s (SDH);

- a connectionless data service (CBDS/SMDS) serving over 50 sites, based on a DQDB platform interconnecting MAN switching systems (MSS) nodes, and using its own transmission system (34.386 and 139.264 Mbits/s PDH).

CBDS has been commercially available since the end of 1993, the second element of SuperJanet being a Closed User Group on that service. BT has started the migration of CBDS onto an ATM platform which can also offer (see Figure 4.6):

- CBR service over AAL type 1 to carry H.261 video streams;

- Variable Bit Rate (VBR) service to carry X.25 data streams.

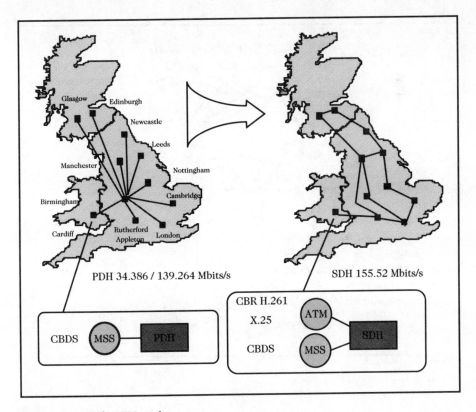

Figure 4.6   BT's ATM trials

4.5.2   Deutsche Bundespost Telekom

Two MANs based on DQDB have been commercially available in Munich and Stuttgart (DATEX-M) since 1993 and extension to eight cities has recently been achieved. DBT's ATM national pilot project provides ATM nodes in three main cities: Berlin (Siemens), Köln (Alcatel/SEL) and Hamburg (Ericsson), see Figure 4.7.

Each of these comprises one ATM VP cross-connect and two remote multiplexers. A Permanent Virtual Path service is now available and tariffed. DBT is the first European operator to release a tariff for ATM services. A Switched Virtual Circuit service is expected early in 1995. Interworking with ISDN and PSDN is planned for late 1995, when ATM-based services are expected to be commercially available. Extension to at least 50 nodes should further increase service availability beyond 1996.

The MAN islands and the national ATM trial will be connected to the MoU trial.

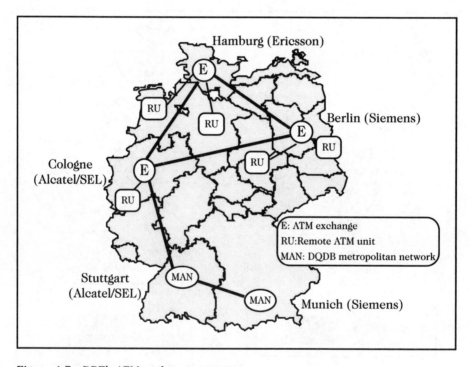

Figure 4.7 DBT's ATM trials

4.5.3 France Telecom

France Telecom is running a pilot network, named BREHAT, based on ATM multiplexers from TRT, a French subsidiary of Philips, and ATM VP cross-connects from CIT/Alcatel. CBDS will be the initial service for LAN interconnection and 2.048 Mbits/s circuit emulation and videoconferencing should also be provided. Services are expected to be available either on the port side of the so-called ATM service multiplexer or over digital links transporting continuous cell streams at 34.386 Mbits/s.

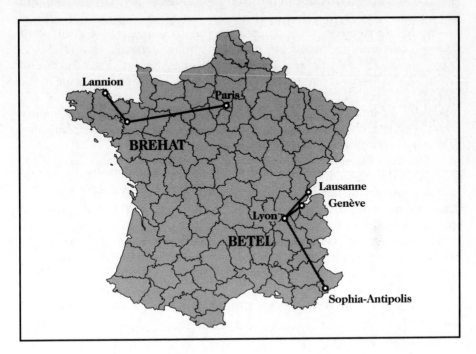

Figure 4.8   France Telecom ATM trials

We should also mention the BETEL trial which was the first international ATM connection over 34.386 Mbits/s between four sites: IN2P3 (Lyon), EPFL (Lausanne), CERN (Geneva) and EURECOM (Sophia-Antipolis). (See Figure 4.8.)

Deutsche Bundespost Telekom and France Telecom will run a bilateral pilot project linking their national ATM trials in addition to the European trial already agreed through the MoU.

4.5.4   Other broadband trials in Europe

A MAN based on DQDB is available in Brussels. It is aimed at providing services to hospitals, academic institutions and banks. This MAN will be bridged to the MoU trial. A CBDS server capability is needed on top of the ATM VP cross-connect function.

The Danish telecommunication sector has been reorganized and the situation is not yet fully clarified. Nevertheless, two companies are participating in the MoU trial. Two nodes are available, one in Copenhagen and one in Aarhus, purchased from Alcatel and Siemens, respectively; the node in Copenhagen is also the international gateway. Beyond CBDS and circuit emulation, KTAS, one of the local companies involved in the trial, will test a frame relay service over ATM.

The Italian situation remains complex due to the existence of different network operators for national and international services. Several MANs based on DQDB are offered by SIP in Florence, Naples, Pisa, Turin and Trieste. An ATM trial is planned in Milan and other major cities. Owing to the current structure of the Italian telecommunication sector, SIP is not reponsible for international connections, while IRITEL is the MoU signatory body. The SIP MAN islands and the SIP national ATM trial will be connected to the MoU trial through IRITEL.

A Finnish ATM network is operational between Helsinki and Tampere. It is connected to the MoU trial.

The situation in the Netherlands is very similar to that in Britain: the academic network, called Surfnet, will be upgraded to ATM capability and will become Surfnet 4.

The presence of two operators in Portugal also leads to different trials: Telecom Portugal has two MANs (also based on DQDB) in Aveiro and Coimbra and Telephones de Lisboa-Porto has two MANs based on DQDB in Lisbon and Oporto.

Last but not least, a MAN based on DQDB is being trialled in Madrid by Telefonica.

4.5.5 ATM in the United States

Telecommunications operators, such as interexchange carriers and Bell regional holding companies, are implementing new network infrastructures based on ATM technology for switching components and SDH for transmission components. This new infrastructure will provide high bandwidth and support dramatically changing traffic patterns. Such an infrastructure is divided into sub-networks:

• a core network based on both ATM and SDH;

• an access network to maximise the number of Points of Presence (PoP) for the operator, as well as the number of services offered to the end user.

This two tier strategy leads to the gradual deployment of ATM and is aimed at providing the business customers with multiple services through the PoP node. A number of interexchange carriers, such as AT&T, GTE and MCI, are running customer trials in 1994 and are planning commercial services in 1995. Some special service providers have already opened up

ATM services: MFS Datanet (Metropolitan Fiber System) and WilTel, who also pioneered frame relay bearer services a few years ago. Both have agreements with local carriers to connect business customers to their nearest PoP node. These services remain limited in terms of services to permanent virtual circuits and, in terms of coverage, to few large cities. A number of trials are still underway to evaluate a broader use of the ATM technology in support of broadband services. Among them, four can be viewed as major ATM trials in the wide area networks domain:

- the National Research and Education Network (NREN), which consists of a number of broadband test beds that have been up and running for a few years;

- the California Research and Education Network (CALREN), which also includes ATM switches and application test beds;

- the US West' COMPASS (COMmunications Program for Advanced Switched Services) trial, which could be viewed as an on-going activity in terms of telecommunications technology, since it started with ISDN and now embraces ATM;

- the North Carolina broadband superhighway project, in which the State takes an active role in promoting the deployment of a telecommunications infrastructure to support broadband applications, providing a justification for Public Network Operators (PNOs) to deploy ATM technology. It implies a public/private sector partnership with major PNOs in North Carolina: Bell South, GTE and Sprint/Carolina telephone.

5

ATM and local area networks

5.1   The development of local area networks

After a decade of growth, conventional local area networks are changing
rapidly, due to the pressure of increased demand for transfer capacity. The
idea of sharing the network's capacity, which is the very basis of IEEE 802
type networks, is being rendered obsolete by the increasing requirements of
individual connected workstations. Resource sharing is gradually being
replaced by the concept of centralized switching. Consequently, star wiring
topologies are gradually replacing bus and ring topologies.

A simple observation illustrates this tendency: though the number of
local area networks continues to increase rapidly, the number of stations per
network is declining. This indicates that the transfer capacity offered (4, 10
or 16 Mbits/s depending on type) is less and less susceptible to sharing,
because the stations are consuming more of the bandwidth. The limit is
reached when there is only one station left on the local area network. This
tendency reinforces the growth of local area networks because, if the number
of stations per local area network decreases, more and more local area
networks are required to connect the increasing number of stations.

There are two possible approaches to interconnecting these segmented local area networks:

- use another local area network with a higher bit rate to connect the local area network segments;

- use a central switching unit.

The first solution continues the principle of resource sharing and distributed switching (for example, FDDI). It means that new local area networks must be introduced regularly to interconnect the previous generations.

The second has the advantages of centralization and allows a large number of stations and/or local area network segments, of whatever type, up to the capacity of the switching unit. In contrast to the technologies used in the IEEE 802 type networks, which are all based on a maximum capacity which has to be shared, a central switching unit provides a granular and virtually unlimited capacity.

The latter approach proves to be more flexible in an environment where there are a large number of stations of different types, whose needs for capacity are growing; whereas the sharing of transfer resources implies a certain stability of demand and minimum homogeneity of machines. This return to central switching for local area networks means that a switching technology will have to be chosen. Everything seems to point to ATM as the best possible choice. This technology, when used in a local environment, will be found in the **hub**.

Given the great demand for means of interconnecting stations and local area network segments, the area in which ATM technology develops rapidly should be local area networks, long before wide area networks.

In this scenario, where the private domain is in advance of the public domain, the use of a standard ATM technology poses the problem of a competent standardization authority. The ATM Forum was created by a number of manufacturers to fill this gap and to speed up the creation of standards which serve the needs of the private domain, while retaining compatibility with those being drawn up for the public domain.

Two things will play a fundamental role in the development of ATM local area networks:

- the kind of wiring used between the stations and the hub;

- the capability to make the stations and the hub work in a unchanged mode from the applications' point of view.

Using this approach, called *LAN emulation*, the conventional IEEE 802 type interfaces can be replaced by ATM interfaces without disturbing the existing applications. We will discuss wiring and LAN emulation in greater detail in the next two sections.

5.2 Wiring a site

Apart from fibre optics, which are still reserved for very high bit rates, and coaxial pairs, whose use is declining, the main medium used for wiring sites is the twisted pair (see Figure 5.1).

Internal telephone connections, for example to a private exchange, are usually made with 'voice' quality twisted pairs, whose impedance is about 100 ohms. These pairs can also be used, subject to restrictive conditions of distance, for connecting data stations to a local area network. The maximum bit rate, over a distance of 1 km, is about 100 kbits/s.

Data transmissions are usually carried over 'data' quality twisted pairs. Their characteristic impedance is about 150 ohms at the frequencies involved; they can be shielded (**STP**, *Shielded Twisted Pairs*) or unshielded (**UTP**, *Unshielded Twisted Pairs*) and the bit rates can reach several Mbits/s over a kilometre. Shielding surrounds either each pair in the cable or all the pairs. It is a kind of metal tube, called a screen, and is effective at high frequencies (several MHz). There may also be a copper wire mesh around the pairs. This mesh is effective at low frequencies, and may, therefore, be used along with the screen.

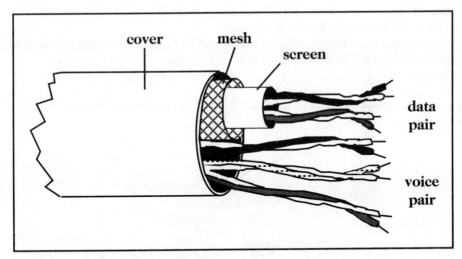

Figure 5.1 Cable with metallic pairs

Reuse of UTP quality pairs, which are frequently used for wiring sites, is a desirable aim, if ATM technology is to be introduced without disturbance. It is not easy to make the 155.520 or 622.080 Mbits/s speeds, used for user–network access to long-distance services, compatible with the UTP wiring environment, and few local applications are capable of justifying such speeds. Therefore, lower bit rates are proposed for bringing ATM technology to the workstation. Thus, a proposition has been made for an access speed of 25.6 Mbits/s, using 4B/5B coding to represent information transferred at a

32 Mbaud modulation rate, that is, the equivalent of a 16 Mbits/s bit rate with Manchester or Differential Manchester coding. Other speeds are also proposed, in particular 51.84 Mbits/s on UTP quality pairs and 100 Mbits/s, mainly on fibre optics (see page 84).

5.3   LAN emulation

We should remind ourselves of the principles of IEEE 802 local area networks, in order to better understand the role of ATM technology. They provide a communication medium for a set of devices which use an access protocol, so that they can share the capacity. They are mainly of two types:

- CSMA/CD bus at 10 Mbits/s, conforming to the IEEE 802.3 standard (ISO 8802-3), using coaxial cable or twisted pair (10BaseT);

- token ring at 4 or 16 Mbits/s (IEEE 802.5 or ISO 8802-5), mainly based on twisted pair wiring.

FDDI 100 Mbits/s networks, also structured as a ring using fibre optic or twisted pairs, are suitable for very high speed stations, but are also used to connect conventional local area networks.

In contrast to a bus, a ring requires the use of an active connector to attach each station and, whenever a station is disconnected, continuity has to be ensured. This can be done by using hubs, which include relays for isolating

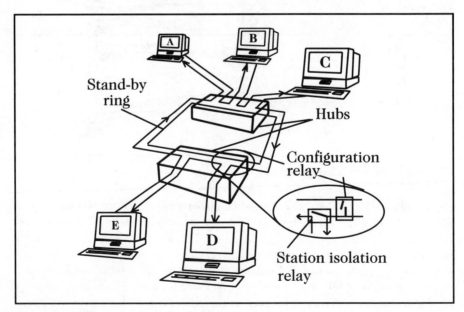

Figure 5.2   Physical wiring of a ring

each station. Furthermore, they often allow for a stand-by ring, which is used to reconfigure the ring, via other relays, if there is a cut-off. Figure 5.2 shows how this kind of wiring scheme gives the ring a tree structure.

Hubs like these may also be present on CSMA/CD buses, especially of the 10BaseT type. In every case, they make it easier to install and administer the connected stations.

There can be various reasons for separating a local area network into several segments: demand for bandwidth, restricting distance, number of stations, different bit rates, and so on. These segments are usually linked by interconnecting units (bridges or routers). If hubs are installed, they are particularly suited to hosting these interconnection functions.

5.4   Intelligent hubs

As the functions carried out by hubs have increased, they have gradually become the key devices in local area networks – intelligent hubs: when the number of segments that need to be interconnected becomes too large, a switching function becomes essential in these devices. In the context of such centralized switching, it is interesting to mention some hybrid technical solutions: the bandwidth of a IEEE 802 type connection is then totally dedicated to a single station, MAC frame switching being carried out in the hubs. Another approach consists in choosing ATM switching technology, which is capable of satisfying data applications as well as multimedia applications or interactive video. This choice has the added advantage of technological compatibility with long–distance networks.

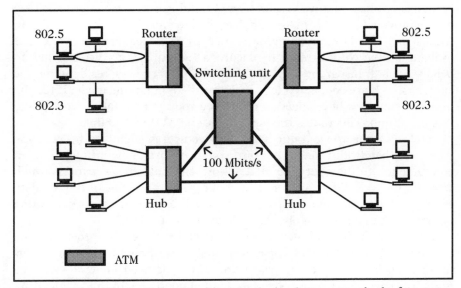

Figure 5.3   Introducing ATM technology into the local area network: the first stage

As Figure 5.3 shows, at first the ATM switching unit interconnects compatible segments to give the appearance of a continuous local area network which has not been segmented. On each segment, the stations continue to work in their own mode, for example IEEE 802.5. The intelligent hubs can be connected to each other in ATM mode via a 100 Mbits/s interface using the FDDI physical layer (see page 31).

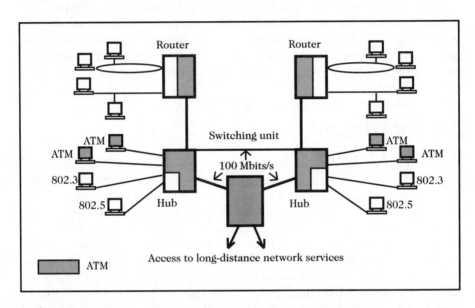

Figure 5.4   Introducing ATM technology into the   local area network: the second stage

In a later phase, native ATM 25.6 or 51.84 Mbits/s interfaces (see page 81) can be provided by the intelligent hub for connecting the stations working in ATM mode. This last configuration is then an ATM local area network. The evolving scenario, illustrated by Figure 5.4, means that the hub has to behave in a transparent way *vis-à-vis* the applications resident on the stations which are connected to it, whatever their operating mode: IEEE 802 or ATM. This type of connection requires a routing function located in the intelligent hub. This routes the MAC frames on ATM virtual links.

ATM does not provide an explicit flow control mechanism, because the necessary bandwidth must be reserved *a priori*. This principle is in contradiction to the operating mode of present local area networks, which work on the 'best effort' principle, without prior knowledge of the capacity required. This principle must be preserved if a smooth transition, which protects investments in applications, is to be made.

A simple flow control mechanism must be introduced in order to avoid over-dimensioning transfer capacities and congesting the network. This mechanism is similar to the congestion signalling used in ATM switching units (see page 58). We must emphasize the importance of this mechanism, because the loss of a cell due to congestion affects a much larger data unit, which may be several thousand bytes long. This means that if one cell is lost due to congestion, all the cells belonging to that data unit have to be retransmitted.

An explicit flow control signal will resolve this problem and preserve the principle of local area networks: access to the total transfer capacity for each user, without having to predetermine a restrictive contracted capacity. A congestion signal allows the transfer of cells to be stopped under the control of the ATM switching node. It is accompanied by a restart signal. Congestion control can be selective and only apply to a given virtual connection; or it can be global and apply to all the existing virtual connections that pass through a particular interface. This principle implies a choice, for all virtual connections, between two operating modes:

- connections operating in reserved mode, based on an explicit capacity contract;

- connections operating in *best effort* mode, based on the absence of any contract, and requiring an explicit flow control mechanism (see page 17).

Appendix

ATM standardization

CCITT

The CCITT (International Consultative Committee on Telegraphy and Telephony) is one of the standardization bodies of the ITU (International Telecommunications Union). Its members are representatives of the member countries of the ITU (France Telecom for France), and certain scientific and industrial organizations. The CCITT is now called **TSS** (*Telecommunication Standardization Sector*).

The CCITT's standardization work is defined in plenary sessions which are held every four years. It is then carried out by *Study Groups* (**SG**) which are themselves made up of **Working Parties** (*WP*). The group concerned with ATM is SG 13 (*Digital Networks Including ISDN*) and, more especially, WP 8 which is responsible for broadband ISDN. CCITT documents are called Recommendations. The first ones concerning ATM were approved in 1988: they are Recommendations I.113 (*Vocabulary of Terms*) and I.121 (*Broadband Aspects of ISDN*).

CCITT has defined ATM as the target transfer mode for broadband ISDN. A large number of Recommendations relating to ATM or broadband ISDN have been approved or are about to be; the main ones are listed below:

I.113	*Vocabulary of Terms;*
I.121	*Broadband Aspects of ISDN;*
I.150	*ATM Functional Characteristics;*
I.211	*Service Aspects;*
I.311	*General Network Aspects;*
I.321	*Protocol Reference Model;*
I.327	*Network Functional Architecture;*
I.35B	*ATM Layer Performance Aspects;*
I.361	*ATM Layer Specification;*
I.362	*AAL Functional Description;*
I.363	*AAL Specification;*
I.364	*Support of Broadband Connectionless Data;*
I.371	*Traffic Control and Resource Management;*
I.413	*User–Network Interface (UNI);*
I.432	*UNI Physical Layer Specification;*
I.555	*Frame Relay Interworking;*
I.610	*OAM Principles of B-ISDN Access;*
Q.142x	*Metasignalling;*
Q.2761/4	*NNI Signalling;*
Q.21x0	*Service Specific Connection Oriented Protocol;*
Q.2931	*UNI Signalling;*
Q.SAAL	*AAL for Signalling;*
F.811	*Service Description Connection Oriented Data;*
F.812	*Service Description Connectionless Data.*

ANSI

Like AFNOR in France, **ANSI** (*American National Standards Institute*) is the United States national standardization body. It has a vast field of activity and delegates its authority to an appropriate body for each domain. **ECSA** (*Exchange Carriers Standards Association*) is the accredited body for telecommunications.

ANSI committee T1 is in charge of telecommunications. In particular, this committee issued the standards relating to **SONET** (*Synchronous Optical NETwork*), acting on a proposition from **Bellcore** (*Bell Communications Research*). The T1S1 technical group is more especially concerned with high speed networks.

The standards concerning broadband ISDN are usually the equivalent of the CCITT Recommendations (see the list below):

T1.105	*Synchronous Optical Network;*
T1E1.2/92-020	*UNI PMD Specifications;*
T1S1/92-185	*UNI Rates and Formats;*
T1S1.5/92-002	*ATM Layer Specifications;*
T1S1.5/92-003	*AAL 3/4 Common Part;*
T1S1.5/92-004	*AAL for CBR (Class A) Services;*
T1S1.5/92-005	*Support of Connectionless Services;*
T1S1.5/92-006	*Services Baseline Document;*
T1S1.5/92-007	*Generic flow control (GFC);*
T1S1.5/92-008	*VBR AAL Service Specific Part;*
T1S1.5/92-009	*Traffic and Resource Management;*
T1S1.5/92-010	*AAL 5 Common Part;*
T1S1.5/92-029	*OAM Aspects (Technical Report);*
T1S1.5/92-xxx	*AAL Architecture for Class C/D and Signalling.*

ANSI committee X3, which is in charge of computer networks and interfaces, is also heavily involved in ATM. Its X3T9.5 subgroup set the FDDI standard; similarly, the documents relating to **HIPPI** (*HIgh Performance Parallel Interface*) and to FCS were published by the X3T9.2 subgroup.

IEEE

This organization (*Institute of Electrical and Electronics Engineers*) is well known for its local area network standards, formulated by Project 802. IEEE group 802.6 issued the DQDB protocol standard, for metropolitan area networks: it uses cells of the same size as ATM cells. Further, the 802.9 group, responsible for the connection of terminals to local and long-distance networks, is also interested in the work on ATM.

ATM Forum

The ATM Forum was formed in 1991 and currently includes about 500 companies. Its main mission is to speed up the development and deployment of ATM products through interoperability specifications. The ATM Forum produces implementation agreements based on international standards; another goal is to fill in the gaps in specifications when standards are not available.

The current ATM Forum specifications are the following:

- User–Network Interface (UNI);
- Broadband InterCarrier Interface (B-ICI);
- ATM Data eXchange Interface (DXI).

The UNI specification defines an ATM bearer service based on virtual connections, either permanent or switched (UNI Signalling), with declarable bandwidth and/or Quality of Service (QoS). It also includes an Interim Local Management Interface (ILMI) with a protocol based on the SNMP network management standard. The UNI specification applies to the following physical layer interfaces :

* public 155.520 Mbits/s interface with OC-3 coding;

* public 44.736 Mbits/s interface with DS-3 coding;

* private 100 Mbits/s TAXI interface with 4B/5B FDDI coding;

* private 155.520 Mbits/s interface with 8B/10B FCS coding.

The B-ICI specification defines a multi-service carrier-to-carrier interface to support:

* cell relay service;

* circuit emulation service;

* frame relay service;

* switched multimegabit data service (SMDS).

The DXI specification describes the data link control protocol and physical layers between a DTE (such as a router) and an ATM Data Service Unit (ATM-DSU) seen as a DCE. It also defines a Local Management Interface (LMI) and a Management Information Base (MIB).

ETSI

The aim of **ETSI** (*European Telecommunication Standards Institute*) is to draw up European standards called **ETS** (*European Telecommunication Standards*). Whenever possible, these documents use existing standards as their basis (for example, CCITT standards) and, once they are approved, they apply to all the member countries of ETSI. The following list gives the correspondences between the CCITT recommendations and the standards approved by the members of ETSI:

ETS 300.298	I.361	*ATM Layer Specification;*
ETS 300.299	I.362	*AAL Functional Description;*
ETS 300.300	I.363	*AAL Specification;*
ETS 300.301	I.432	*UNI Physical Layer Specification.*

Bibliography

Armbruster H. (1993). *The Flexibility of ATM*. In *Proceedings of the ATM Conference*, and Paris, April

Boisseau M., Demange M. and Munier J.-M. (1994). *High Speed Networks*. Wiley

De Prycker M. (1990). Asynchronous Transfer Mode: Solution for Broadband ISDN. Ellis Horwood Ltd

Handel R., Huber M.N. and Schroder, S. (1994). *ATM Networks: Concepts, Protocols, Applications*. Addison-Wesley

Tanenbaum A. (1989). *Computer Networks*. Prentice Hall

Coudreuse J.-P. et al. (1991). *Spécial ATM*. L'Echo des recherches n° 144/145

Macchi C. and Guilbert J.-F. (1987). *Téléinformatique*. Dunod

Nussbaumer H. (1988). *Téléinformatique (2 vols)*. Presses Polytechniques Romandes

Pujolle G. (1992). *Télécommunications et réseaux*. Eyrolles

Further References

Cuthbert, L.E. and Sapanel J.C. (1993). *ATM: The Broadband Solution*. IEE

Kyas, O. (1994). *ATM Networks*. International Thomson Publishing

Thematic index

A

adaptation
 ATM 16; 32
  AAL type 1 34
  AAL type 2 38
  AAL type 3/4 38
  AAL type 5 42
  SAAL 68
addressing
 signalling 70
 OAM virtual path 46
 VPI, VCI 19

B

broadcasting 7
 broadcast 53
 multicast 53
 signalling 70

C

connection mode
 connectionless service 19
 connection-oriented service
  AAL type 3/4 38
  AAL type 5 42
  ATM 18, 54

E

error correcting
 FEC 34, 37
error detecting
 CRC 35, 38, 41, 42, 45
 HEC 18, 26, 32

F

flow control
 assured mode 39
 back pressure 58
 best effort 84, 85
 GFC 17, 18, 66
 traffic contract 20

non-assured mode   39
admission control   21
Cell Loss Priority   18, 21, 47
congestion notification   23
discarding   24
rate policing   22
spacing   21

P
projects
  BETEL   75
  Deutsche Bundespost Telekom   73
  European   71
  France Telecom
    BREHAT   74
    Prélude   2
  IBM
    PARIS   2
  USA   76

S
signalling
  DSS-1   68
  metasignalling   20; 70
  SS-7
    B-ISUP   69
    ISUP   69
standards
  ANSI   88
  ATM Forum   14, 31, 80, 89
  CCITT   5, 7, 14, 25, 37, 87
    G.709   66
    G.711   47; 48
    G.727   47
    G.804   30
    I.113   88
    I.432   29
    I.610   44
    Q.142X   70

    Q.21X0   68
    Q.2761/4   69
    Q.761/4   69
    Q.921   68
    Q.931   68
  ECSA   88
  ETSI   90
  IEEE   89
    802   79, 80, 82
    802.3   82
    802.5   82, 84
    802.6   30
  ISO
    8802-3   82
    8802-5   82
switching
  circuit switching   2, 51
    STM   6
  packet switching   2, 52
  cell relay
    ATM   6, 15, 16, 32
    DADB   16

T
transfer
  asynchronous
    ATM   21, 71
    ATM cell jitter   32
  isochronous
    FDDI-II   13
  plesiochronous
    PDH   31
  synchronous
    SDH   6, 25, 29, 44, 61
    SONET   4
transfer technology
  fibre optics   9, 11, 81, 82
  twisted pair   81, 82

Index of abbreviations

A

AAL	ATM Adaptation Layer	16
AIS	Alarm Indication Signal	44
ANSI	American National Standards Institute	88
ATD	Asynchronous Time Division	3
ATM	Asynchronous Transfer Mode	6

B

B-ISUP	Broadband Integrated Service User Part	69
B-LT	Broadband Line Termination	63
B-NT1	Broadband Network Termination 1	64
B-NT2	Broadband Network Termination 2	64
B-TE	Broadband Terminal Equipment	64
B-TA	Broadband Terminal Adaptor	64
BBTG	BroadBand Task Group	5
BIP	Bit Interleaved Parity	44
BSVC	Broadband Signalling Virtual Channel	70

C

CLNAP	ConnectionLess Network Access Protocol	41
CLP	Cell Loss Priority	18

95

CLSF	ConnectionLess Service Function	**41**
CMI	Coded Mark Inversion	**66**
CPCS	Common Part Convergence Sublayer	**39**
CPI	Common Part Indicator	**40**
CS	Convergence Sublayer	**34**

D

DCC	Digital Cross-Connect	**19**
DQDB	Distributed Queue Dual Bus	**16**
DSS-1	Digital Signalling System-1	**68**

E

ECSA	Exchange Carrier Standards Association	**88**
EFCN	Explicit Forward Congestion Notification	**23**
ETS	European Telecommunication Standards	**90**
ETSI	European Telecommunication Standards Institute	**90**

F

FCS	Fibre Channel Standard	**31**
FDDI	Fibre Distributed Data Interface	**13**
FEBE	Far End Block Error	**44**
FEC	Forward Error Correction	**34**
FERF	Far End Receive Failure	**44**
FIFO	First In First Out	**56**
FPS	Fast Packet Switching	**3**

G

GFC	Generic Flow Control	**17**

H

HEC	Header Error Control	**18**
HIPPI	HIgh Performance Parallel Interface	**89**
HLPI	Higher Layer Protocol Identifier	**42**
HOL	Head Of Line blocking	**56**

I

IEEE	Institute of Electrical and Electronics Engineers	**89**
ISUP	Integrated Service User Part	**69**

M

MAC	Medium Access Control	**2**
MID	Multiplexing IDentification	**41**

N

NNI	Network Node Interface	**17**
NRZ	Non Return to Zero	**66**

O

OAM	Operation, Administration and Maintenance	**45**

P

PBX	Private Branch eXchange	**64**
PDH	Plesiochronous Digital Hierarchy	**25**
PLCP	Physical Layer Convergence Protocol	**30**
POH	Path OverHead	**30**
PTI	Payload Type Identification	**18**

Q

QOS   Quality Of Service   42

R

RTS   Residual Time Stamp   35

S

SAAL   Signalling ATM Adatation Layer   68

SAR   Segmentation And Reassembly sublayer   34

SDH   Synchronous Digital Hierarchy   6

SDU   Service Data Unit   39

SG   Study Group   87

SN   Sequence Number   34

SNP   Sequence Number Protection   34

SONET   Synchronous Optical NETwork   4

SRTS   Synchronous Residual Time Stamp   35

SSCOP   Service Specific Connection Oriented Protocol   68

SSCS   Service Specific Convergence Sublayer   39

ST   Segment Type   41

STM   Synchronous Transfer Mode   6

STP   Shielded Twisted Pair   81

T

TAXI   Transparent Asynchronous Xmitter-receiver Interface   31

TEI   Terminal End-point Identifier   70

TSS   Telecommunication Standardization Sector   87

U

UNI   User Network Interface   17

UTP   Unshielded Twisted Pair   81

V

VCI   Virtual Channel Identifier   19

VPI   Virtual Path Identifier   19

W

WBC   WideBand Channel   13

WP   Working Party   87

FORE
Systems